DEVELOPING MATHEMATICS

CW00382359

Photocopiable teaching resources for mathematics

COUNTING AND UNDERSTANDING NUMBER

Ages 7–8

Hilary Koll and
Steve Mills

A & C Black • London

Contents

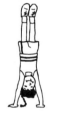

Published 2008 by A & C Black Publishers Limited
38 Soho Square, London W1D 3HB
www.acblack.com

ISBN 978-0-7136-8444-5

Copyright text © Hilary Koll and Steve Mills 2008
Copyright illustrations © Trevor Metcalf 2008
Copyright cover illustration © Piers Baker 2008
Editors: Lynne Williamson, Marie Lister, Margie Finn
and Louise Sterno
Designed by HL Studios, Oxford and Susan McIntyre.

The authors and publishers would like to thank Corinne McCrum
and Catherine Yemm for their advice in producing this series
of books.

A CIP catalogue record for this book is available from the British Library.

Printed and bound in Great Britain by Martins the Printers, Berwick-on-Tweed.

A & C Black uses paper produced with elemental chlorine-free pulp, harvested from managed sustainable forests.

Introduction

100% New Developing Mathematics: Counting and Understanding Number is a series of seven photocopiable activity books for children aged 4 to 11, designed to be used during the daily maths lesson. The books focus on the skills and concepts for Counting and Understanding Number as outlined in the Primary National Strategy *Primary Framework for literacy and mathematics*. The activities are intended to be used in the time allocated to pupil activities in the daily maths lesson. They aim to reinforce the knowledge and develop the skills and understanding explored during the main part of the lesson, and to provide practice and consolidation of the objectives contained in the Framework document.

Counting and Understanding Number

This strand of the *Primary Framework for mathematics* is concerned with helping pupils to develop an understanding of the relationships between numbers and the way our number system works. It includes all aspects of counting, ordering, estimating and place value, and involves building awareness of how numbers can form sequences and can be represented on number lines and in grids. Also included in this strand of the curriculum is work on negative numbers, fractions, decimals, percentages and ratio and proportion. Broadly speaking, this strand addresses topic areas that were described under the 'Numbers and the Number System' strand title of the former National Numeracy Strategy *Framework for teaching mathematics*.

Counting and Understanding Number Ages 7–8 supports the teaching of mathematics by providing a series of activities to develop essential skills in counting and recognising numbers. The following objectives are covered:

- read, write and order whole numbers to at least 1000 and position them on a number line; count on from and back to zero in single-digit steps or multiples of 10;

- partition three-digit numbers into multiples of 100, 10 and 1 in different ways;

- round two- or three-digit numbers to the nearest 10 or 100 and give estimates for their sums and differences;

- read and write proper fractions, e.g. $\frac{3}{7}$, $\frac{9}{10}$, interpreting the denominator as the parts of a whole and the numerator as the number of parts; identify and estimate fractions of shapes; use diagrams to compare fractions and establish equivalents.

Extension

Many of the activity sheets end with a challenge (**Now try this!**), which reinforces and extends children's learning, and provides the teacher with an opportunity for assessment. These might include harder questions, with numbers from a higher range, than those in the main

part of the activity sheet. Some challenges are open-ended questions and provide opportunities for children to think mathematically for themselves. Occasionally the challenge will require additional paper or that the children write on the reverse of the sheet itself. Many of the activities encourage children to generate their own questions or puzzles for a partner to solve.

Organisation

Very little equipment is needed, but it will be useful to have available: coloured pencils, dice and spinners, counters, cubes, scissors, glue, coins, squared paper, number lines, number grids and number tracks.

Where possible, children's work should be supported by ICT equipment, such as number lines and number tracks on interactive whiteboards, or computer software for comparing and ordering numbers. It is also vital that children's experiences are introduced in real-life contexts and through practical activities. The teachers' notes at the foot of each page and the more detailed notes on pages 6 to 11 suggest ways in which this can be effectively done.

To help teachers select appropriate learning experiences for the children, the activities are grouped into sections within the book. However, the activities are not expected to be used in this order unless stated otherwise. The sheets are intended to support, rather than direct, the teacher's planning.

Some activities can be made easier or more challenging by masking or substituting numbers. You may wish to re-use pages by copying them onto card and laminating them.

Accompanying CD

The enclosed CD-ROM contains electronic versions of all the activity sheets in the book for printing, editing, saving or display on an interactive whiteboard. Our unique browser-based interface makes it easy to select pages and to modify them to suit individual pupils' needs. See page 12 for further details.

Teachers' notes

Brief notes are provided at the foot of each page, giving ideas and suggestions for maximising the effectiveness of the activity sheets. These can be masked before copying.

Further explanations of the activities can be found on pages 6 to 11, together with examples of questions that you can ask. Solutions can be found on pages 63 and 64.

Whole-class warm-up activities

The tools provided in A & C Black's *Maths Skills and Practice* CD-ROMs can be used as introductory activities for use with the whole class. In the *Maths Skills and Practice CD-ROM 1* the following activities and games could be used to introduce or reinforce 'Counting and Understanding Number' learning objectives:

- *Patterns 1*
- *Patterns 2*
- *Snowboarding*
- *Fractions*
- *Mad ratty*
- *Fractions 2*
- *Place value*

The following activities provide some practical ideas which can be used to introduce or reinforce the main teaching part of the lesson, or provide an interesting basis for discussion.

Larger/smaller

With the class sitting in a circle, ask a child to say a number between 500 and 1000. The next child should say a number that is larger than this. The next child in the circle should say one that is smaller than the new number, working around in a circle, e.g. 705, 895, 894, 900, 300, 413, 324... To add an extra level of difficulty, explain that the children can only use the digits 4, 7 and 5 in their answers, e.g. 475, 754, 744, 755, 444, 557, 555, etc. Record the numbers on the board and see how many numbers can be written in this way using the digits without a number being repeated.

Run-around

Around the walls of the hall or classroom, pin pieces of paper showing 0 and the multiples of 100 from 100 to 1000. Ask the children to stand in the middle of the room and call out three-digit numbers. Ask them to round the number to the nearest hundred and run to the correct sign. This can be played as a game where children who are standing by incorrect signs are out.

As a further activity, children could be asked to stand by a sign and give a number that would correctly round to this multiple.

Crocodile

Invite two children to the front of the class with some place value cards. Give each child a three-digit number to make using the cards. Invite a third child to be the greedy crocodile and to come to the front and stand facing the child with the larger number, holding arms to represent the crocodile's mouth. Demonstrate how this can be recorded, e.g. 157 > 127 or 156 < 157. Point out that the mouth is always open towards the larger number.

Superheroes

Choose two children to stand at the front. Explain that these children are superheroes! As you face them, the girl on the right would be Ones Woman, the boy in the middle would be Tens Man and the child on the left, Hundreds Man/Woman. Explain that each superhero is responsible for part of a number: Tens Man is responsible for the tens, etc.

Write a three-digit number on the board and ask each superhero to collect their part of the number using base 10 materials (such as Dienes blocks). To make a superhero 'disappear' children must take away all the block he or she is holding. For example, for 384 to make Tens Man vanish we must take away 80 (8 tens) rather than just 8. Continue in this way until each superhero has disappeared. Repeat this process, using other children and a variety of three-digit numbers.

Calculator heroes

The activity above can be played using a calculator. Children key in a three-digit number and then must get rid of the digits one at a time leaving an empty space or a zero. They do this by subtracting an amount. If they have been introduced to the superheroes, encourage them to talk of this digit as, 'I'm going to make Hundreds Man disappear'. This helps to reinforce the idea that the position of the digits is significant and affects the value of the digit.

5

Notes on the activities

Read, write and order whole numbers to at least 1000 and position them on a number line

The ability to read three-digit numbers that are written in figures relies heavily on an understanding of place value, that is, an understanding that the position of a digit determines its value. For example the 7 in 173 represents 7 tens (70), whereas the 7 in 754 represents 7 hundreds (700). If children have not fully grasped this concept, then they are likely to confuse 405 with 450 and so on.

Some children may find writing numbers in words difficult because of spelling and language difficulties. Check whether they are able to say the number names correctly, for example knowing that 89 is 'eighty-nine' or 532 is 'five hundred and thirty-two'. When writing numbers in words, watch out for common spelling errors such as 'fourty', 'ninty' 'fiveteen', 'eightteen' etc.

Having a mental picture of number lines is vital in developing an awareness of how numbers relate to each other. This awareness underpins all mental calculation and it is very important that children have a wide range of experience of comparing and ordering numbers and positioning them on number lines. Ensure that a full range of number lines, segments and tracks are available around the classroom for children to refer to.

Tortoise bingo (page 13)

As the children fill in their grid, encourage them to show their numbers to a partner as an additional check that their numbers lie within the number range suggested. It is common for children to forget the number range and to write numbers outside it. For the extension activity, have clearly displayed the correct spellings of the number names of numbers to 20 and multiples of 10 to 100. (Children's routes across the grid should go from left to right.)

SUGGESTED QUESTIONS:

- What number does this word say?
- How do you spell 90/40/17?

Number cards (page 14)

Different games and activities can be played.

Individual activities

1) Pelmanism – place all the cards face down and turn over pairs (one of each shape). If the numbers match, keep them; if not, turn them back face down and continue.

2) Ordering – pick four cards and put them in order of size, smallest first. Record the numbers in words and in figures.

Games for two

1) Pelmanism – as above. The player with the most pairs wins.

2) Snap – one child should have the number name cards and the other should have the number in figures. If two cards show the same value, the first to say 'Snap' wins the cards.

3) Snap variation – using only the cards showing numbers in figures, 'Snap' is called when two numbers in the pair show the same number of hundreds, tens or units, for example 118 and 538 both have eight ones.

SUGGESTED QUESTIONS:

- Read this number to me. Is it more or less than five hundred?
- How would this number be written in figures/using words?

Code breaker (page 15)

For this activity, it is important to clearly display somewhere in the classroom the correct spellings of the number names of numbers to 20, and multiples of 10 to 100, to which children can refer.

SUGGESTED QUESTION:

- Look at the spelling on the board. Can you see any difference between my spelling and how you have spelt it?

Silly spaghetti (page 16)

The focus of this activity is on reading three-digit numbers in words and then writing them in figures and vice versa. The activity includes numbers where 0 is a place holder, such as 608. Children require a solid understanding of place value to answer this type of question correctly.

SUGGESTED QUESTIONS:

- How many tens are there in one hundred and thirty-seven? How many ones? How many hundreds?
- How would you say this number?
- Read this number to me. How would you write that number?

More or less (page 17)

For this activity, ensure that the children are familiar with the 'greater than' and 'less than' symbols by revising them at the start of the lesson. Write a number and the 'less than' sign, for example 246 < ? and ask the children to state numbers that could go to its right. Discuss that there are hundreds and hundreds (an infinite number) of possibilities. Show how the number of possibilities could be narrowed by writing another sign to the right, for example 246 < ? < 300. Explain that the first part of the inequality (246) must be less than the new number, and the new number must be less than 300. Write further inequalities in the same way. Ask the children to describe the number range in words.

Greater and less (page 18)

To play this game, the children lay the shuffled < cards face down in one pile, the shuffled > cards face down in another pile and the plain number cards in a pile. They take it in turns to take two cards from the arrow piles and one card from the plain number pile. If they can make an inequality with two of the cards, such as 911 > 731, they score two points. If they can use all three cards, for example 911 > 731 > 385, they score three points. When they have finished their turn, they return their cards to the bottom of the appropriate piles. The player with the most points at the end of ten rounds is the winner.

SUGGESTED QUESTIONS/PROMPT:

- Which of these numbers is the smaller? Which is the larger?
- Which sign is this?
- Tell me a number greater/less than 384/467/609.

Riddle reasoning (page 19)

See the notes for 'More or less' above as a means of introducing the notation 234 < ? < 497.

Show how to narrow down the information to find the unknown number by drawing an empty number line and writing on it each number in the questions, with an arrow to show which side of the number the unknown will lie. For example, for the first question they could draw:

20 →   25 →   37 →   ← 39   ← 42   ← 50

This shows that the only whole number possible is 38.

SUGGESTED QUESTION:

- Read this inequality to me. What number or numbers could it be?

Word order (page 20)

When ordering the numbers, remind the children to compare the hundreds digits first, then the tens, and finally the units to work out the order of the numbers.

SUGGESTED QUESTIONS:

- Which of these numbers is the smallest? Which is the largest? Which numbers come in between them?

Paper people (page 21)

This activity can be started practically. Fold a long strip of paper into a zigzag and cut sections out along the folded edges. Open out the strip and write numbers in order along the row. This can form an interesting display. One number could perhaps be incorrectly placed and the children could be asked to find the mistake.

SUGGESTED QUESTIONS/PROMPT:

- Which is the largest/smallest number? Write these in first.
- How many tens/ones has this number?

Dot to dot (page 22)

To introduce this activity, write a range of about ten numbers between 400 and 499 (inclusive) randomly on the board. Ask the children to come to the front to join the numbers in order, starting with 400. When they reach 499, begin a new game, writing numbers from 800 to 899.

SUGGESTED QUESTIONS/PROMPT:

- Did you find this work easy or difficult? Why?
- Find the largest number on the sheet.

Animal antics (page 23)

Some children might find it easier to write multiples of 10 along each line to help them place the joining lines more carefully. Encourage the children to check each other's work once the lines have been placed. For the extension activity, ensure the children realise that there can be more than one acceptable answer for each and discuss their answers as a class at the end of the lesson.

SUGGESTED QUESTIONS:

- Have you checked your answers?
- Which number do you think this might be?

Number line lotto (page 24)

For this activity, each pair of children will need three dice. It is better if the dice are numbered 1 to 6 rather than represented with dots, as they can be placed next to each other to form the three-digit number more effectively. This sheet could also be copied onto A3 and a small group of children could play together.

SUGGESTED QUESTIONS:

- Do you think your partner's number is correct?
- Between which two multiples of 10 does the number lie?

Monkey puzzles (page 25)

To provide further similar worksheets, the numbers could be altered on the CD. Watch out for children who think that 1010 is less than 910 as the sum of its digits is smaller. This common error demonstrates a lack of understanding of place value ideas.

SUGGESTED QUESTIONS:

- Where on the line would you mark the number 652?
- Between which two multiples of 10 does it lie?

Piggy in the middle (page 26)

Support the children who are finding this activity difficult by asking them to count up from the lower number to the higher and to write these numbers down, and then choose one of the numbers they have written. Alternatively, point to the sheep numbers on a number line to 1000, and ask the children to say the numbers in between. Hide the number line, and ask the children to pick one of the numbers that they had read.

SUGGESTED QUESTIONS:

- Which number lies between these two?
- Are there other numbers it could be?
- What is the lowest/highest number it could be?

Count on from and back to zero in single-digit steps or multiples of 10

This aspect of counting and understanding number begins with children counting forwards and backwards in different-sized steps and develops into recognising, continuing and explaining sequences. By focusing on counting on from and back to zero, multiples of 2, 3, 4, 5, ... can be explored. This is a vital part of repeated addition and early multiplication and helps children to begin to recognise and memorise multiplication facts.

Encourage the children to use number lines and grids to help them to explore sequences, and to look for patterns in the digits which will help them to become more effective in recognising and explaining sequences.

Spider web (page 27)

The children should only fill in a section when it is landed on, rather than filling all the numbers in a section working inwards. Filling in numbers as they land on them requires a greater number of attempts at counting forwards and backwards and can help the children to become more familiar with the sequences.

SUGGESTED QUESTIONS:

- What number do you think will come next?
- What is 10 more than 40? 100 less than 800?

Necklace numbers (page 28)

When counting back in twos from 56, encourage the children to continue moving around the circle in a clockwise direction from the start number (56) rather than reversing the direction.

This sheet could also be used by children to help them practise counting forwards and backwards in ones.

SUGGESTED QUESTION/PROMPT:

- Did you find counting back in twos more difficult?
- Check your answers with a partner.

Swimming lanes (page 29)

Draw the children's attention to the fact that some sequences involve counting on and others involve counting back.

SUGGESTED QUESTIONS/PROMPT:

- What is 10 more than 100? Find it on your sheet.
- What is 10 less than 160?
- What do you notice about the ones digits of the numbers in the sequence?
- What if the sequence started on the number one, counting on in tens?

Catch! (page 30)

This activity can be played as a practical activity as part of a PE lesson or in the classroom, passing around an object rather than throwing a ball.

SUGGESTED QUESTION:

- What is 5 more than/less than 150?

Don't take a fence! (page 31)

After the children have completed the activity, they could use the constant function on a calculator to help them to generate the numbers in these sequences. Begin by keying in 0 followed by ++3 (on most calculators). By continuing to press the = key the display will show the numbers in the sequence. Draw children's attention to the fact that some sequences involve counting on and others involve counting back. Ask children to find the sum of the digits of each number on the sheet, for example for 27, 2 + 7 = 9. Encourage them to notice that the sum of the digits of any multiple of 3 will be 3, 6 or 9.

SUGGESTED QUESTIONS/PROMPTS:

- What is 3 more than 27? Find it on your sheet.
- What is 3 less than 57?
- Tell me about the ones digits of the sequence numbers.
- Which of these numbers is not a multiple of 3? 27, 36, 52, ... Use your sheet to help you check.

Camel train (page 32)

When counting on and back in fours to and from zero, draw attention to the fact that the units/ones digits of numbers are all even in a sequence. Encourage the children to use this as a checking strategy.

SUGGESTED QUESTIONS/PROMPT:

- What is 4 more than 16?
- Which of these numbers is not a multiple of 4? 24, 36, 42, ... Use your sheet to help you check.

Dance class (page 33)

This activity encourages children to begin to recognise which numbers are multiples of 6 and which are not.

SUGGESTED QUESTION/PROMPT:

- Which of these numbers is not a multiple of 6? 24, 36, 42, 56, ... Use your sheet to help you check.

Dragon boat race (page 34)

After completing the activity sheet, the children could use the constant function on a calculator to help them to generate the numbers in these sequences. Begin by keying in the first number of the sequence followed by ++7 = = = = = = ... or – – 7 = = = = ...

Fitness fun (page 35)

This sheet involves repeated addition, which can be done by counting on in steps of 7, 8 and 9. If appropriate, as a checking tool, children could be introduced to multiplication, for example checking the first part by multiplying 7 by 7.

SUGGESTED QUESTIONS:

- How many lots of 7 are there?
- Is there another way we could check?

Plenty of twenties (page 36)

It might be helpful for some children to write the multiples of 20 between 0 and 300 onto the number line at the start of the lesson to assist them with this work.

SUGGESTED QUESTIONS:

- When counting on in 20s, what number comes after 200/160/240?
- When counting on in 20s, what number comes before 200/160/240?

Mixed up, missed out! (page 37)

When children begin counting on in steps that are multiples of 10, such as in steps of 20, 30 or 40, encourage them to use what they already know about counting on in twos, threes or fours. If they know 2, 4, 6, ... they should be encouraged to see the link with that and 20, 40, 60, ...

SUGGESTED QUESTIONS:

- How many are we counting on each time in this sequence?
- What is 20/30/40 more than 120?

Multiple octopus (page 38)

A multiple octopus can be a permanent feature on the wall of any classroom. It can serve as a useful focus for a mental/oral activity, where you call out a number and the children say whether this number is a multiple of 2, 3, 4, 5, 6, 7, 8 or 9 by looking at the legs of the octopus. It can help the children to see that some numbers are common to more than one set of multiples. Note that in the extension activity, the children are asked to say which octopus leg(s) the numbers appear in, rather than listing all the numbers that are factors, for example 36 is not on the twos or threes legs but yet are factors of 36. If appropriate, discuss how the legs could be extended to include further multiples.

SUGGESTED QUESTIONS:

- Is this in the sevens octopus leg?
- Does 23 appear in any of the legs?
- Is 42 a multiple of 6?

Changing the guard (page 39)

This activity can be introduced practically. Ask the children to stand (or sit) in lines of ten, perhaps in the hall. Call out a multiple of 10 and ask the children in turn to count back in equal-sized steps, for example from 30 in threes. When the end of the line is reached, the front child should march to the back and a new multiple of 10 given. Continue in this way so that the children get a variety of questions of varying difficulty.

Partition three-digit numbers into multiples of 100, 10 and 1 in different ways

> An understanding of the ideas of place value is essential if children are to become confident in dealing with numbers to 1000 and beyond. Appreciating that the first digit in a three-digit number represents the number of groups of hundred, whereas the last digit represents the number of ones/units is vital. It is also important that children know that 3 hundreds is the same as 300 and that 6 tens is the same as 60, and so on.
>
> In order to be confident with adding and subtracting numbers, the children need to be aware that numbers can be partitioned (split) in many different ways. It is also important that they learn how to partition a three-digit number into hundreds, tens and ones, and this partitioning is particularly useful when adding pairs of two- and three-digit numbers.

Superheroes (page 40)

This activity enables children to practise partitioning three-digit numbers. For children who find this difficult, you could provide place value cards and write H, T and U above the numbers on the sheet. Ask the children to say the number in words before they try to split it, for example 'two hundred and sixty-two'. As they say each part of the number, they can take the appropriate place value cards and place them on the table so that they can see how the number is made up.

SUGGESTED QUESTIONS:

- What amount is *Hundreds Man* in charge of?

- What do you notice about the amount *Tens Girl* is in charge of in the number 605?

Partition pots: 1 and 2 (pages 41–42)

The cards could also be used for a variety of place value activities, such as finding two cards with the same tens digit, for example 743 and 841.

SUGGESTED QUESTIONS/PROMPT:

- How many tens has this number?
- Find me a card with two hundreds and two ones. What is the value of the tens digit?

Digit snap! (page 43)
Game rules

- Remove the jokers, jacks, queens and kings from a pack of playing cards and share out the pack.
- Both players say 'turn!' and then at the same time put three cards onto their sheet to make a three-digit number.
- As soon as all the cards are shown they shout 'snap!' if the two numbers have the same number of hundreds, tens or units (for example 428 and 368 have the same number of ones). The first player to shout 'snap!' correctly and say which digit(s) are the same, records both numbers on their sheet and wins the cards from both sheets.
- If 'snap!' is not called, players keep putting new cards on their sheets, placing them on top of the others.
- The winner is the player with all the cards, or with the most cards when 15 number pairs have been recorded.

SUGGESTED QUESTIONS:

- How many tens has this number?
- Can you find a number with three hundreds/tens/ones?
- Do any two numbers have the same 'hundreds' digit and the same 'tens' digit, such as 534 and 537?
- What is the difference between the two numbers?
- James has the numbers 236 and 536. How many less than 536 is 236?

Partition patterns (page 44)

Partitioning in different ways, using multiples of 100, 10 and 1, underpins the most commonly used method of subtraction, known as decomposition. When subtracting 159 from 381 using a written method, the 381 can be changed to 3 hundreds, 7 tens and 11 ones so that the 9 ones in 159 can be subtracted.

SUGGESTED QUESTION/PROMPT:

- The pattern is moving ten across each time. What will the next number in the pattern be?

Matchmakers (page 45)

The cards could be photocopied onto thin card and laminated to provide a more permanent classroom resource.

SUGGESTED QUESTIONS/PROMPT:

- Have you sorted the cards into groups? Now arrange the cards in one group into an order.

- What is the total of each card in this group?
- How could you continue this pattern further?

Hedgehog numbers (page 46)

Again, this activity encourages the children to develop confidence in partitioning numbers into multiples of 100, 10 and 1 in different ways.

SUGGESTED QUESTIONS:

- How did you work out which number goes in the hedgehog?
- How else could you split that number?

Going crackers! (page 47)

This activity can be used throughout the year for checking children's understanding of the number system. As a further extension, the children could make up their own 'cracker' puzzles with suggested answers for someone else to try.

SUGGESTED QUESTIONS/PROMPT:

- Which digit has changed between these two numbers?
- Add 1 to this number to check your answer.
- How many more is 583 than 183? How can you tell?

Round two-digit or three-digit numbers to the nearest 10 or 100 and give estimates for their sums and differences

> When rounding to the nearest 10, ensure the children understand that the answer will always be a multiple of 10 or zero, for example 0, 10, 20, 30, 40, and so on.
>
> When rounding to the nearest 100, ensure the children understand that the answer will always be a multiple of 100 or zero, for example 0, 100, 200, 300, 400, and so on.

Lifebelts (page 48)

Practise counting in tens from 0 to 100 and back again. Ask the children to say a number that is less/more than a given multiple of 10, and then move on to asking children to say which multiple of 10 a given number rounds to.

SUGGESTED QUESTIONS:

- Can you find a number that ends in the digit 5 on your sheet?
- Do numbers ending in the digit 5 round up or down?

Rounders (page 49)

Explain to the children that, although there are more squares than circles on the number line, there are no numbers that round down to 300, so there is an equal chance of squares or circles winning.

Note that the sheet could be enlarged onto A3 and laminated to provide a more permanent resource.

SUGGESTED QUESTION:

- What multiple of 10 is this nearest to?

Rounding machine (page 50)

The children work out for themselves which hundreds number a number rounds to. Children who are finding this difficult could refer to a number line to 1000, marked only in hundreds.

SUGGESTED QUESTIONS/PROMPT:

- Do numbers ending in 50 round up or down?
- Show me on this 300 to 600 number line where 456 would be. Which hundreds number is it closest to?

Whose dog? (page 51)

As a further extension, the children could draw more dogs on the sheet and write three-digit numbers between 350 and 949 on their sides. They should then join them to the appropriate owner by rounding the numbers to the nearest 100.

SUGGESTED QUESTIONS:

- Do numbers ending in 50 round up or down?
- Which multiple of 100 is this nearest to?

Round and about (page 52)

This activity involves approximating answers to two-digit addition and subtraction questions. The children should round the numbers to the nearest 10 and write them onto the teacups above, before adding the two multiples of 10 together to provide an approximation for the question.

Introduce and use a range of vocabulary, for example: roughly, about, estimate, round, approximate.

SUGGESTED PROMPT:

- Say roughly what the answer to this question would be.

Rain rounding (page 53)

Similarly, this activity involves rounding to the nearest 100 and using these approximations to estimate the answer to the addition or subtraction. The children could find the exact answers, using a written method or a calculator, to see how close their estimates were.

SUGGESTED PROMPT:

- Say roughly what the answer to this question would be.

Have a good trip! (page 54)

This activity involves rounding distances to help when estimating a total. Discuss with the children why this sort of rounding and estimating is useful in everyday life, and ask them to give other examples of situations where the exact answer is not needed.

SUGGESTED QUESTION:

- About how many kilometres have they travelled on this journey?

Read and write proper fractions, interpreting the denominator as the parts of a whole and the numerator as the number of parts; identify and estimate fractions of shapes; use diagrams to compare fractions and establish equivalents

Understanding fractions is an important part of later mathematics work. From an early age, children begin to hear the words 'half' and 'quarter' in everyday language, but need to refine their understanding of what is meant by them. In everyday conversation one might hear the phrase 'I'll have the bigger half' which can lead to mathematical misunderstandings: two halves must be the same size so neither can be bigger! Children need to experience fractions in a wide range of contexts, where fractions are seen as areas of shapes, parts of a set, on number lines and as the result of a division operation, to develop a full understanding of them.

At ages 7 and 8, children should begin to appreciate the role of the numerator and denominator, and widen their knowledge of fractions beyond halves and quarters.

Tile teasers (page 55)

For the extension activity, provide the children with large isometric paper and ask them to cut out shapes made from triangles and shade them, writing what fraction of each shape is shaded. These help children to appreciate that the denominator shows how many triangles there are in the whole shape.

SUGGESTED QUESTION/PROMPTS:

- Shade that tile. What fraction of the shape is shaded now?
- Draw me a shape that has $\frac{2}{5}$ shaded.

Magic carpets (page 56)

It is important that children appreciate that the number on the bottom of a fraction indicates the number of equal parts into which the whole has been split.

The children could also play a memory pairs game where they place the cards face down and take it in turns to turn two over. If they match, the cards are won. The winner is the player with the most cards at the end.

SUGGESTED QUESTIONS:

- How many equal parts are there altogether?
- How many are shaded?

Gee-up horse! (page 57)

As children's answers are estimates they will vary considerably.

SUGGESTED QUESTION:

- Can the fraction be described in more than one way?

Fraction wall (page 58)

Ensure the children appreciate that the number on the top of the fraction, the numerator, tells them how many of the pieces to count along from the left, for example $\frac{3}{8}$ means 3 of the eighths-rods. Also ensure that they are confident with the > and < signs.

SUGGESTED QUESTION/PROMPT:

- Find another fraction that is equivalent.
- Which is larger? How can you tell?

Clever cylinders (page 59)

To give further practice to children who are finding this concept difficult, reproduce several copies of the cylinder diagrams and provide different-coloured pencils. The children could colour equivalent fractions the same, for example $\frac{5}{20}$, $\frac{1}{4}$ and $\frac{2}{8}$ could all be coloured red; $\frac{2}{10}$, $\frac{1}{5}$ and $\frac{4}{20}$ could all be coloured green.

SUGGESTED QUESTION:

- Can you find another fraction that is equivalent/worth the same?

Equivalent cards (page 60)

The cards can be used to play different games and activities.

Individual activity

Place all the cards face down and turn over pairs. If the fractions are equivalent, keep the cards, if not turn them face down. The winner is the player with the most pairs at the end.

Pair games

1) One child takes the cards with the diagrams to the right of the fractions and the other takes the cards with the diagrams to the left. If two cards are equivalent, the first to say 'snap!' wins the cards.

2) Place all the cards face down and take turns to turn over pairs. If the fractions are equivalent, keep the cards, if not turn them face down. The winner is the player with the most pairs.

SUGGESTED QUESTION:

- Can you say another fraction that is equivalent/worth the same?

Yo-ho-ho! (page 61)

At the start of the lesson, write a range of unit fractions (those with the numerator 1) on the board. Call out a number and point to an appropriate fraction, for example 12 and $\frac{1}{4}$, and ask the children to find one-quarter of 12. Demonstrate how this can be done practically, by sharing 12 counters into four equal groups. Point out that it can also be done mentally by dividing 12 by 4.

SUGGESTED QUESTIONS/PROMPT:

- What is one-quarter of 12?
- Find one-sixth of 60 by dividing 60 by 6. What is the answer?

Colourful kaleidoscopes (page 62)

Many children find shading fractions as areas of a shape very difficult when the number of sections that the shape has been split into does not match the denominator of the shape. For example, when a shape has ten equal parts, they cannot find one-fifth. Show children how to find how many sections to colour. For example, to find $\frac{1}{4}$ of 12 sections count the total number of sections into which the whole has been split (12) and then divide this by the denominator (4). Another method is to use equivalent fractions, for example appreciating that $\frac{1}{4}$ is equivalent to $\frac{3}{12}$.

SUGGESTED QUESTIONS:

- How can you find one-sixth of 12 pieces?
- What is $\frac{1}{4}$ equivalent to?

Using the CD-ROM

The PC CD-ROM included with this book contains an easy-to-use software program that allows you to print out pages from the book, to view them (e.g. on an interactive whiteboard) or to customise the activities to suit the needs of your pupils.

Getting started

It's easy to run the software. Simply insert the CD-ROM into your CD drive and the disk should autorun and launch the interface in your web browser.

If the disk does not autorun, open 'My Computer' and select the CD drive, then open the file 'start.html'.

Please note: this CD-ROM is designed for use on a PC. It will also run on most Apple Macintosh computers in Safari however, due to the differences between Mac and PC fonts, you may experience some unavoidable variations in the typography and page layouts of the activity sheets.

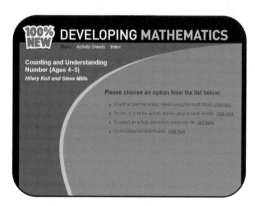

The Menu screen

Four options are available to you from the main menu screen.

The first option takes you to the Activity Sheets screen, where you can choose an activity sheet to edit or print out using Microsoft Word.

(If you do not have the Microsoft Office suite, you might like to consider using OpenOffice instead. This is a multi-platform and multi-lingual office suite, and an 'open-source' project. It is compatible with all other major office suites, and the product is free to download, use and distribute. The homepage for OpenOffice on the Internet is: www.openoffice.org.)

The second option on the main menu screen opens a PDF file of the entire book using Adobe Reader (see below). This format is ideal for printing out copies of the activity sheets or for displaying them, for example on an interactive whiteboard.

The third option allows you to choose a page to edit from a text-only list of the activity sheets, as an alternative to the graphical interface on the Activity Sheets screen.

Adobe Reader is free to download and to use. If it is not already installed on your computer, the fourth link takes you to the download page on the Adobe website.

You can also navigate directly to any of the three screens at any time by using the tabs at the top.

The Activity Sheets screen

This screen shows thumbnails of all the activity sheets in the book. Rolling the mouse over a thumbnail highlights the page number and also brings up a preview image of the page.

Click on the thumbnail to open a version of the page in Microsoft Word (or an equivalent software program, see above.) The full range of editing tools are available to you here to customise the page to suit the needs of your particular pupils. You can print out copies of the page or save a copy of your edited version onto your computer.

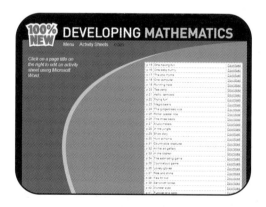

The Index screen

This is a text-only version of the Activity Sheets screen described above. Choose an activity sheet and click on the 'download' link to open a version of the page in Microsoft Word to edit or print out.

Technical support

If you have any questions regarding the *100% New Developing Literacy* or *Developing Mathematics* software, please email us at the address below. We will get back to you as quickly as possible.

educationalsales@acblack.com

Tortoise bingo

- **Your teacher will give you a number range.**
- **Write different numbers from this range in the sections below.**

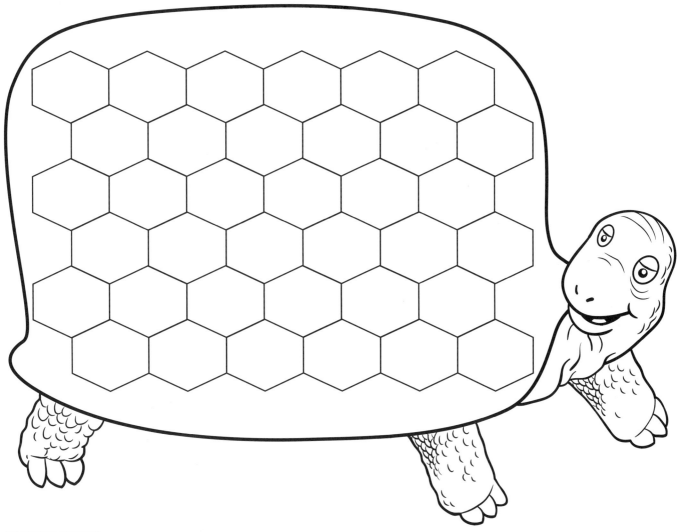

NOW TRY THIS!

- **Choose a route from one side of the grid to another.**
- **Write each number in the route in words on the back of this sheet.**
- **Swap sheets with a partner and find each other's route.**

Teachers' note Provide a number range of about 60 three-digit numbers, such as numbers between 560 and 620. Once the children have filled in the grid, call out random numbers, like bingo, making a note of which you have said. Children should cross out numbers if they have them. The winner is the child who has a route crossed off that goes from one side of the grid to the other.

**100% New Developing Mathematics
Counting and Understanding
Number: Ages 7–8
© A & C BLACK**

• **Cut out the cards and play 'Memory pairs' with a partner.**

one hundred and forty-two	two hundred and seventy-one
three hundred and sixty-four	four hundred and thirty-nine
five hundred and thirty-eight	seven hundred and fifty-five
seven hundred and sixty-six	three hundred and ninety-one
two hundred and forty-nine	five hundred and eighty-four
four hundred and ninety-eight	six hundred and seventy-two
eight hundred and nine	one hundred and eighty-eight
one hundred and eighteen	eight hundred and sixteen

142	271	364	439
538	755	766	391
249	584	498	672
809	188	118	816

Teachers' note These cards can be used for a variety of games, such as snap, Pelmanism (memory pairs) and matching games. Further explanation of these games is given on page 6. Whatever the game, encourage the children to read the number names aloud.

100% New Developing Mathematic
Counting and Understanding
Number: Ages 7–8
© A & C BLACK

Code breaker

• **Write these numbers with one letter in each box.**

200 `t` `w` `o` `h` `u` `n` `d` `r` `e` `d`

511

650

906

580

430

702

116

301

810

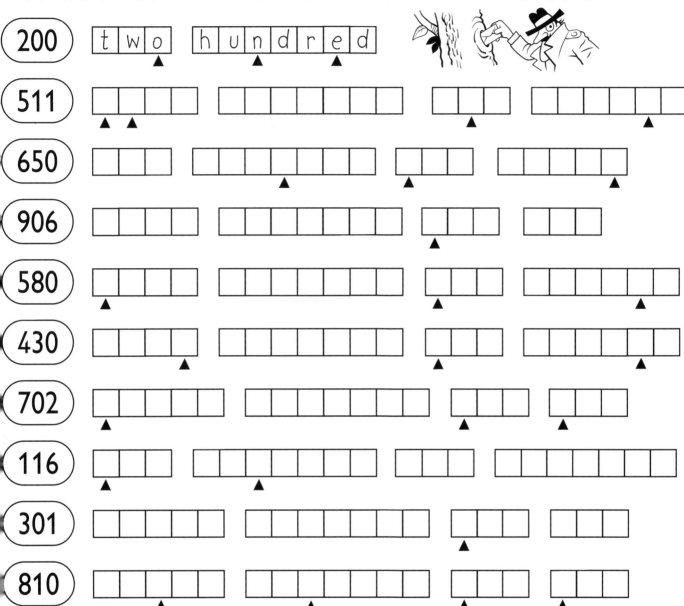

• **Write the letters marked with arrows to spell a sentence.**

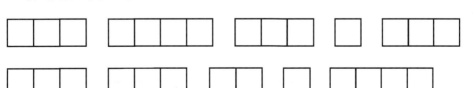

• **Make up a similar puzzle of your own.**

Teachers' note This page contains numbers that contain zero as a place holder and children sometimes experience difficulty in saying the matching number names. Practise these numbers before the children start this activity. Ensure that the children have spellings to refer to.

**100% New Developing Mathematics
Counting and Understanding
Number: Ages 7–8
© A & C BLACK**

15

Silly spaghetti

- Follow the spaghetti and join the children to their plates.
- Write digits on the children and words on the plates.

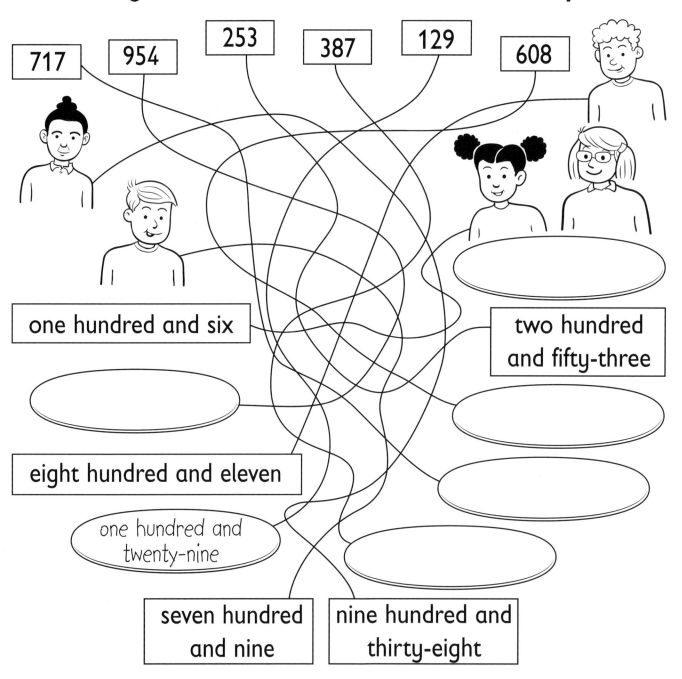

717   954   253   387   129   608

one hundred and six

two hundred and fifty-three

eight hundred and eleven

one hundred and twenty-nine

seven hundred and nine

nine hundred and thirty-eight

NOW TRY THIS!

- Write a pair of matching numbers in the empty spaces and join them with a line.

Teachers' note Ask the children to read the numbers aloud. It is important that they have the spellings of the numbers to refer to. Ensure that these are available on the board or on a display in the room. As a further extension, the children could make up a spaghetti puzzle for a partner to solve.

16

100% New Developing Mathematics
Counting and Understanding
Number: Ages 7–8
© A & C BLACK

More or less

• **Use the clues to help you fill in one digit in each square.**

1		**2** 7	0	**3** 6		**4**		**5**

(crossword grid with entries numbered 1–21)

Across

2. Greater than 705, less than 707
4. ☐ > 157 and ☐ < 159
6. One less than 530
7. Ten more than a multiple of 100
8. 940 < ☐ < 942
11. One less than 610
13. One less than 700
15. 90 < ☐ < 100
18. A multiple of one hundred
19. 940 < ☐ < 945
20. A multiple of ten
21. 578 < ☐ < 580

Down

1. One more than 849
2. One less than 800
3. 640 < ☐ < 650
4. One more than 999
5. One less than 900
9. One less than 480
11. 650 > ☐ > 630
12. One less than 100
14. One more than 900
16. Ten more than 660
17. One less than 600
18. 275 < ☐ < 280
20. 56 > ☐ > 54

Teachers' note At the start of the lesson introduce the 'greater than' and 'less than' signs and show the different ways that a number range can be represented, e.g. ☐ > 157 and ☐ < 159 or 640 < ☐ < 650 or 56 > ☐ > 54. Ensure the children understand that the number range can refer to either one whole number or a set of possible whole numbers.

100% New Developing Mathematics
Counting and Understanding
Number: Ages 7–8
© A & C BLACK

Greater and less

• **Cut out these cards and play with a partner.**

> 134	< 568	> 459
> 801	< 309	< 684
> 555	< 914	420
> 731	< 713	911
> 899	< 950	224
> 385	< 276	672
> 267	< 402	400
> 491	< 437	586

Teachers' note Ensure that the children are familiar with the 'greater than' and 'less than' signs. Please see the activity notes on page 6 for the rules of the game. You could copy the game cards onto card and laminate them to make a more durable resource.

100% New Developing Mathematic
Counting and Understanding
Number: Ages 7–8
© A & C BLACK

Riddle reasoning

• **What whole number is each person thinking of?**

It is between 20 and 50.
It is greater than 37.
It is less than 42.
39 > ☐ and ☐ > 25

38

It is between 100 and 200.
It is less than 198.
It is greater than 192.
180 < ☐ and ☐ < 194

It is between 500 and 700.
It is less than 650.
It is greater than 610.
550 < ☐ < 612

It is between 700 and 800.
☐ < 723
It is greater than 719.
721 < ☐ < 740

☐ < 250
☐ > 230
240 < ☐
248 < ☐ < 252

☐ < 880
☐ > 840
878 < ☐
894 > ☐

☐ < 650
☐ > 600
634 < ☐ < 643
636 > ☐ > 624

☐ < 532
530 > ☐
525 < ☐ < 555
557 > ☐ > 528

NOW TRY THIS!

• **Make up some more riddles of your own for a partner to solve.**

Teachers' note At the start of the lesson introduce the 'greater than' and 'less than' signs and show the different ways that a number range can be represented, for example using words or the notation ☐ > 157 and ☐ < 159 or 640 < ☐ < 650 or 56 > ☐ > 54. Ensure that the children understand that a number range can refer to only one whole number or to a set of possible whole numbers.

100% New Developing Mathematics
Counting and Understanding
Number: Ages 7–8
© A & C BLACK

Word order

- **Write the numbers in order, starting with the smallest, and write each letter on the roof. The letters spell a word.**

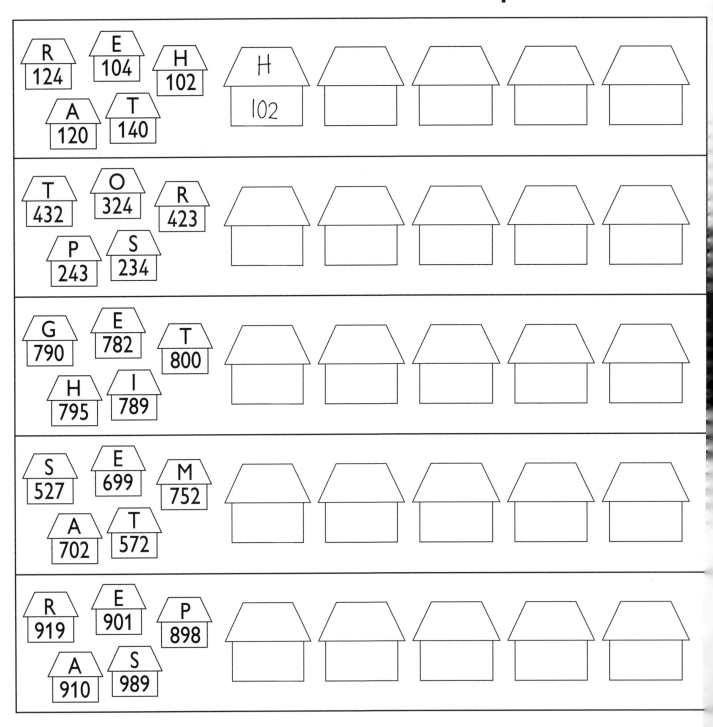

Row 1: R 124, E 104, H 102, A 120, T 140 → first roof H 102

Row 2: T 432, O 324, R 423, P 243, S 234

Row 3: G 790, E 782, T 800, H 795, I 789

Row 4: S 527, E 699, M 752, A 702, T 572

Row 5: R 919, E 901, P 898, A 910, S 989

- **Make up some of your own word order puzzles.**

Teachers' note When the children are making up their own puzzles, encourage them to begin with a five-letter word, such as SPEAR and then to allocate a number for each letter, in order. They should then copy out the numbers, with their corresponding letters, in a jumbled order for their partner to solve. These puzzles can form a stimulating display for classroom visitors to try to solve.

**100% New Developing Mathematic
Counting and Understanding
Number: Ages 7–8
© A & C BLACK**

Paper people

• **Write the numbers in order, smallest first.**

172

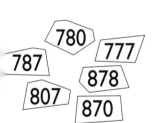

NOW TRY THIS!

• **Write all the numbers on this page that are between 650 and 810.** _____

_____

• **Now write them in order, smallest first.**

_____

Teachers' note Some children may benefit from having a number line or by drawing an empty number line to help them to order these three-digit numbers.

**100% New Developing Mathematics
Counting and Understanding
Number: Ages 7–8
© A & C BLACK**

21

Dot to dot

- **Find the multiples of 100. Join numbers in order from:**
  100 to 199   300 to 399   500 to 599   700 to 799   900 to 999.

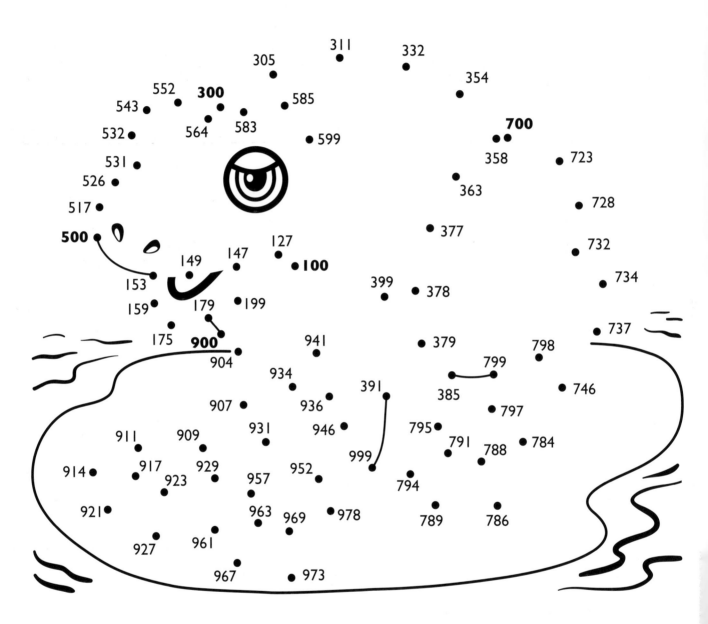

NOW TRY THIS!

- **Write eight numbers in order between 800 and 899.**

22

Teachers' note Explain to the children that not every number between the start and finish points is included. This activity encourages the children to think carefully about how to order numbers and to recognise the value of the hundreds digit as the most significant in a three-digit number.

100% New Developing Mathematics
Counting and Understanding
Number: Ages 7–8
© A & C BLACK

Animal antics

- **Draw a line from each animal to show its position on the number line.**

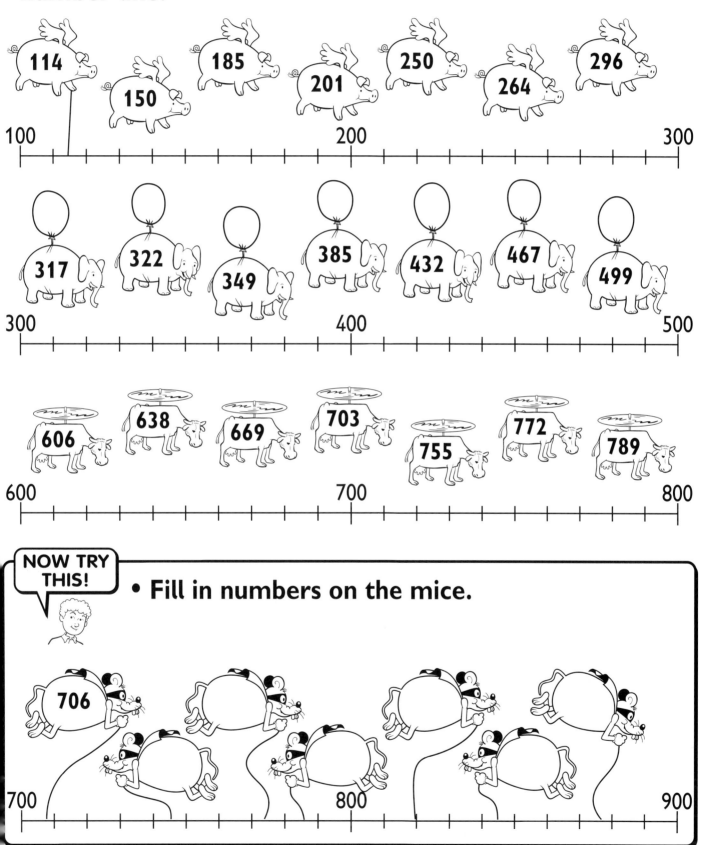

114 **150** **185** **201** **250** **264** **296**

100   200   300

317 **322** **349** **385** **432** **467** **499**

300   400   500

606 **638** **669** **703** **755** **772** **789**

600   700   800

NOW TRY THIS!

- **Fill in numbers on the mice.**

706

700   800   900

Teachers' note At the start of the lesson revise counting in tens from a multiple of one hundred, for example 700, 710, 720, 730... Encourage the children to draw their lines as accurately as they can.

100% New Developing Mathematics
Counting and Understanding
Number: Ages 7–8
© A & C BLACK

Player 1

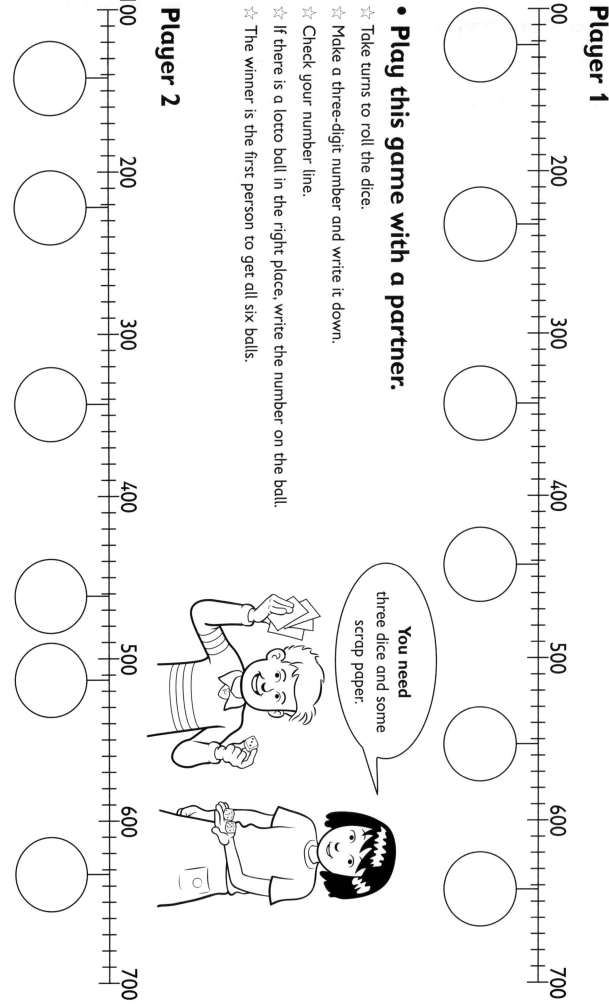

Player 2

• **Play this game with a partner.**

☆ Take turns to roll the dice.

☆ Make a three-digit number and write it down.

☆ Check your number line.

☆ If there is a lotto ball in the right place, write the number on the ball.

☆ The winner is the first person to get all six balls.

You need
three dice and some
scrap paper.

100% New Developing Mathematics
**Counting and Understanding
Number: Ages 7–8**
© A & C BLACK

Teachers' note Explain that the lotto ball positions could be correctly interpreted as perhaps two or three numbers, for example 641, 642 or 643. If every child is given a sheet, each pair could play the game twice, first using child 1's sheet and then child 2's sheet. As an extension activity, the children could be asked to draw five more lotto balls on each line and to write in the numbers.

24

- **The monkeys have been mixing up the numbers.**
  1 Write them in order, smallest first, on the dotted line.
  2 Draw arrows on the number line to show the numbers.

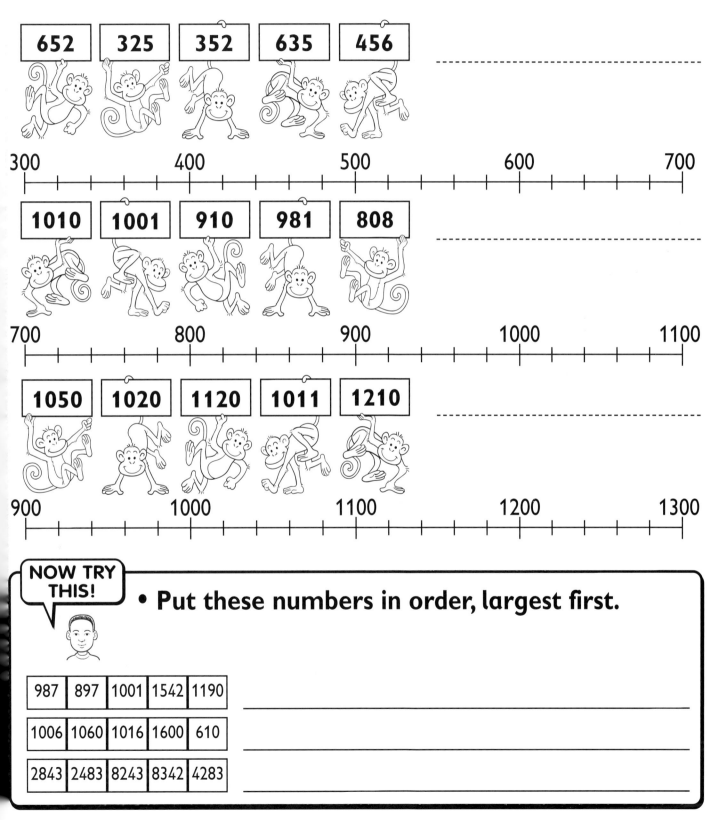

| 652 | 325 | 352 | 635 | 456 |

----

300   400   500   600   700

| 1010 | 1001 | 910 | 981 | 808 |

----

700   800   900   1000   1100

| 1050 | 1020 | 1120 | 1011 | 1210 |

----

900   1000   1100   1200   1300

NOW TRY THIS!

- **Put these numbers in order, largest first.**

987	897	1001	1542	1190

_____

1006	1060	1016	1600	610

_____

2843	2483	8243	8342	4283

_____

Teachers' note At the start of the lesson revise counting in twenties from a multiple of 100, for example: 700, 720, 740, 760. Show how the marks on the number lines above can be labelled by counting in twenties and ask the children to estimate where particular numbers lie on such lines. Encourage the children to draw their lines as accurately as they can.

**100% New Developing Mathematics
Counting and Understanding
Number: Ages 7–8**
© A & C BLACK

25

Piggy in the middle

- On each pig, write a number that lies between the two sheep numbers.

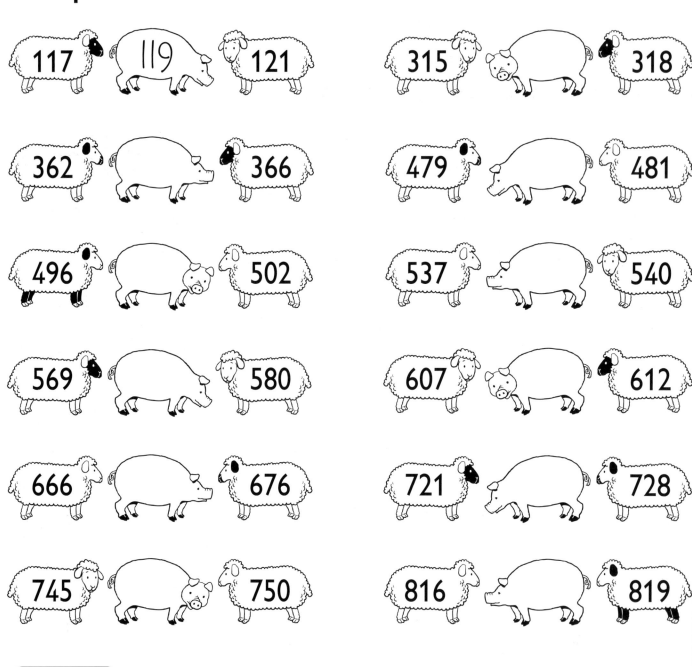

117	119	121	315		318
362		366	479		481
496		502	537		540
569		580	607		612
666		676	721		728
745		750	816		819

NOW TRY THIS!

- Write two sheep numbers that have a difference of 20 and lie either side of the pig number.

787

Teachers' note At the start of the lesson, encourage the children to give numbers that lie between two others. Draw attention to the fact that there can be several numbers that lie between the sheep numbers, or in some cases only one whole number.

100% New Developing Mathematics
Counting and Understanding
Number: Ages 7–8
© A & C BLACK

Spider web

• **You need a counter and a dice.**

☆ Roll the dice and move your counter in a spiral from the centre.

☆ In the space where you land, fill in the number by counting on or back from the number at the edge.

☆ If you land in a space with a fly, go back to the start.

Count on in 10s from 0

Count back in 10s from 120

Count back in 100s from 900

Count on in 1s from 96

Count back in 10s from 89

Count back in 1s from 402

Count on in 100s from 0

Teachers' note Although this is an individual activity, it can also be completed in pairs, with children checking each other's answers as they go along.

100% New Developing Mathematics
Counting and Understanding
Number: Ages 7–8
© A & C BLACK

Necklace numbers

- **Colour the beads.**

Start

blue — green
yellow — yellow
blue — orange
red — green
orange — red
blue — blue
yellow — yellow
green — blue
red — blue — yellow

- **Point to the start bead and say the start number.**
- **Count on in twos as you point to each bead.**

    1 If the start number is zero, write the colour of the bead that is:

    6 ___orange___   14 _____   18 _____

    24 _____   32 _____   44 _____

    2 If the start number is 56, count back in twos and write the colour that is:

    50 _____   42 _____   36 _____

    28 _____   16 _____   0 _____

> **NOW TRY THIS!**
>
> - **If the start number is 100, write the colour that is:**
>
>   98 _____   84 _____   72 _____
>
>   64 _____   58 _____   50 _____

Teachers' note For this activity, the children will need red, orange, yellow, green and blue coloured pencils. When the children count back in twos, check that they count every bead rather than missing a bead out each time (as if counting in ones and just landing on even numbers).

100% New Developing Mathematics
Counting and Understanding
Number: Ages 7–8
© A & C BLACK

Swimming lanes

- **Count on or back in** $\boxed{\text{tens}}$.
- **Write a number on each float.**

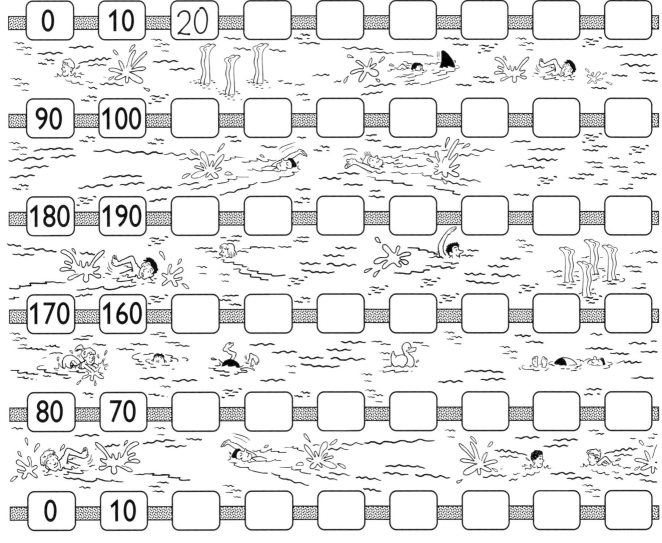

| 0 | 10 | 20 | | | | | | |

| 90 | 100 | | | | | | | |

| 180 | 190 | | | | | | | |

| 170 | 160 | | | | | | | |

| 80 | 70 | | | | | | | |

| 0 | 10 | | | | | | | |

NOW TRY THIS!

- **Count on in** $\boxed{\text{tens}}$.

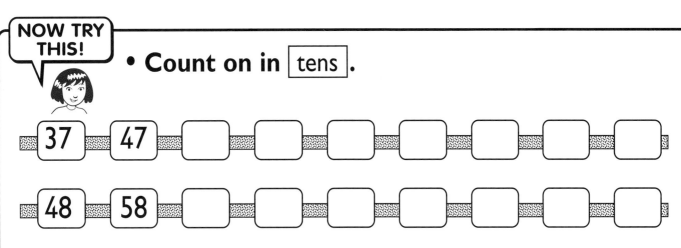

| 37 | 47 | | | | | | |

| 48 | 58 | | | | | | |

Teachers' note Practise counting on and back in tens at the start of the lesson. Draw attention to the fact that the units/ones digit remains the same in any sequence, whatever the start number.

**100% New Developing Mathematics
Counting and Understanding
Number: Ages 7–8
© A & C BLACK**

These children are throwing a ball around the circle.
They count on in | fives | as they catch the ball.

1 Raz calls out '0'. Write the next eight numbers called out.

__5__ ____ ____ ____ ____ ____ ____ ____ ____

2 Sam calls '50'. Write the next eight numbers.

____ ____ ____ ____ ____ ____ ____ ____ ____

3 Josh calls '110'. Write the next 8 numbers.

____ ____ ____ ____ ____ ____ ____ ____ ____

NOW TRY THIS!

• **In a counting back in | fives | game, Lola calls '200'.**
Who will call out the number:

170? _____   155? _____

135? _____   115? _____

100? _____   85? _____

Teachers' note Practise counting on and back in fives at the start of the lesson. Draw attention to the fact that the units/ones digit of numbers in the sequence alternate: 0, 5, 0, 5, 0, 5.

100% New Developing Mathematics
Counting and Understanding
Number: Ages 7–8
© A & C BLACK

Don't take a fence!

- **Count on or back in** [threes].
- **Write a number above each fence post.**

0　　3　　6

27　30

60　　63

99　　96

63　　60

30　　27

NOW TRY THIS!

- **Count back in** [threes].

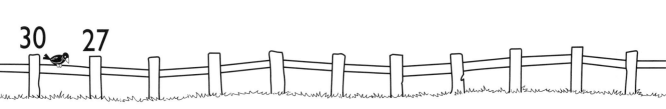

114　117

Teachers' note Practise counting on and back in threes at the start of the lesson. Draw attention to the fact that the units/ones digit of numbers in the sequence alternate between odd and even numbers. Encourage the children to use this as a checking strategy.

100% New Developing Mathematics
Counting and Understanding
Number: Ages 7–8
© A & C BLACK

Camel train

- **Count on or back in** ⬚fours⬚ **to continue each sequence.**

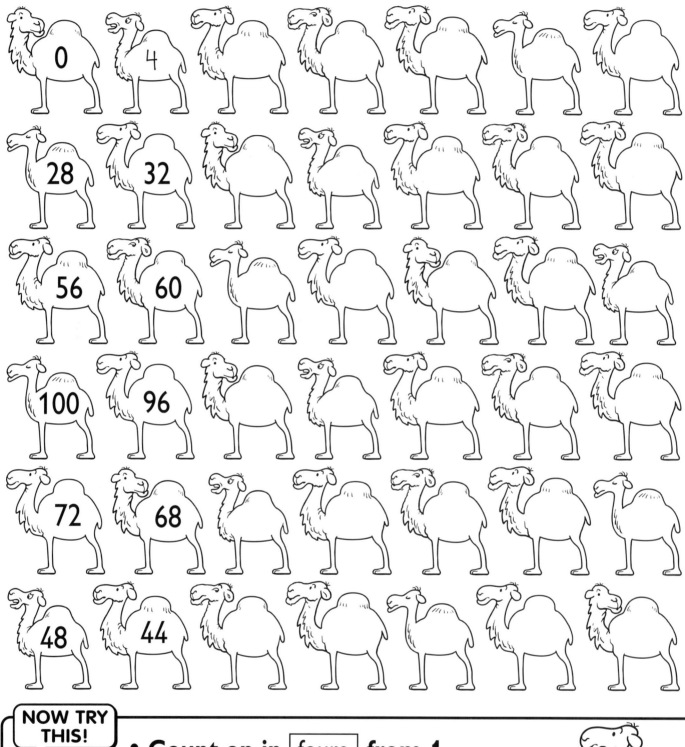

0   4

28   32

56   60

100   96

72   68

48   44

NOW TRY THIS!

- **Count on in** ⬚fours⬚ **from 1.**

_____

32

Teachers' note At the start of the lesson, practise counting on and back in fours to and from zero. Remind children of the fact that the units/ones digits are all even in a sequence and this can be used as a checking strategy. For the extension activity, ensure that the children realise that their answers will not be multiples of 4, and so will not be even.

100% New Developing Mathematics
Counting and Understanding
Number: Ages 7–8
© A & C BLACK

Dance class

- Each sequence should show counting in [sixes] but one number is wrong each time.
- Colour the person with the wrong number.

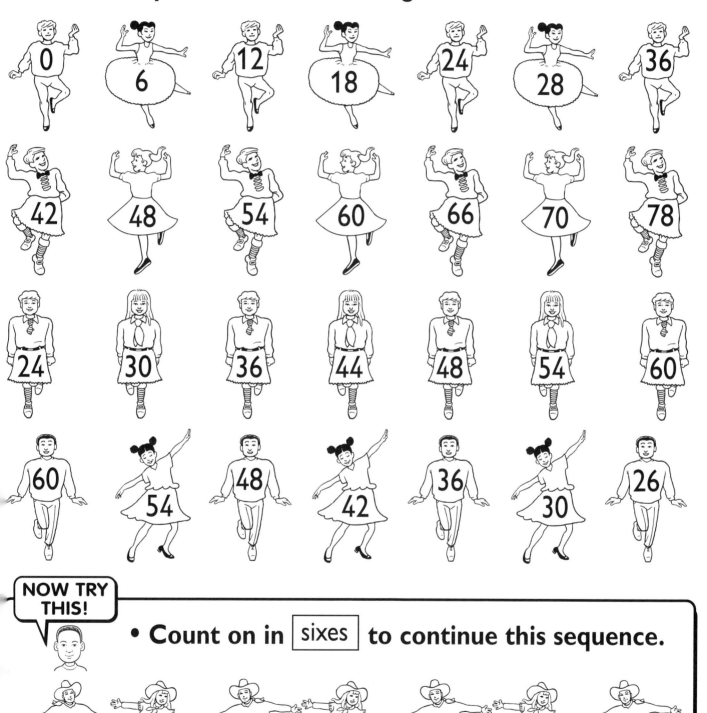

Teachers' note Practise counting on and back in sixes from or back to zero at the start of the lesson. Draw attention to the fact that the units/ones digits of numbers are all even when counting on or back to zero. Encourage the children to use this as a checking strategy.

100% New Developing Mathematics
Counting and Understanding
Number: Ages 7–8
© A & C BLACK

Dragon boat race

• **Count on or back in** ⸢ sevens ⸥ **to continue each sequence.**

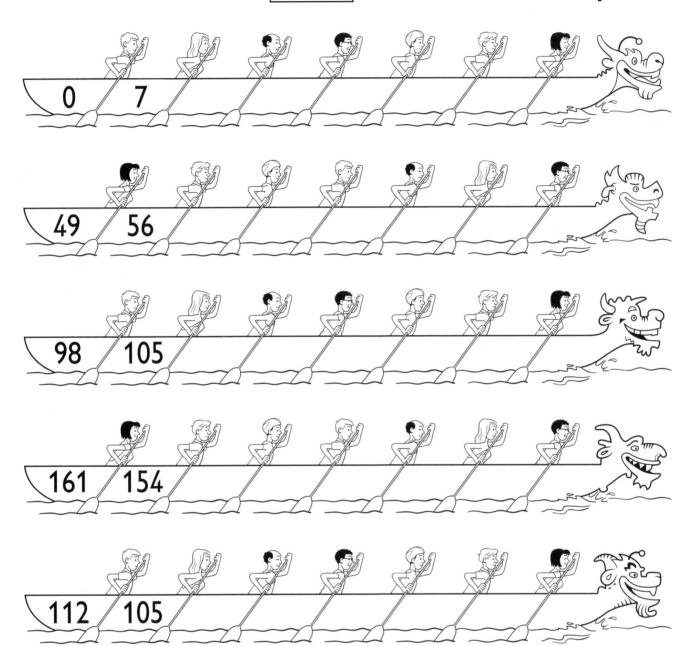

0	7
49	56
98	105
161	154
112	105

NOW TRY THIS!

• **Circle the numbers which are multiples of** ⸢7⸥ **.**

14   32   45   63   93   100   140   147   165   175

Teachers' note Practise counting on and back in sevens at the start of the lesson. Draw attention to the fact that the units/ones digit of numbers in the sequences alternate between odd and even numbers. Encourage the children to use this as a checking strategy.

**100% New Developing Mathematic
Counting and Understanding
Number: Ages 7–8
© A & C BLACK**

Fitness fun

Year 3 are doing some exercises in the school hall.

- Count on to find how many of each exercise is done in total.

The children do 7 skips each. □

They do 8 hops each. □

They do 9 jumps each. □

They do 8 handstands each. □

They do 7 bunny hops each. □

They do 9 splits each. □

They do 8 forward rolls each. □

NOW TRY THIS!

- Continue these sequences.

0   7   14   ___   ___   ___   ___   ___

0   8   16   ___   ___   ___   ___   ___

0   9   18   ___   ___   ___   ___   ___

Teachers' note Practise counting on and back in different-sized steps from or back to zero at the start of the lesson, such as counting in 7s, 8s or 9s. Look for patterns in the digits. Children could point to the artwork as they count.

100% New Developing Mathematics
Counting and Understanding
Number: Ages 7–8
© A & C BLACK

Plenty of twenties

• **Count in** | twenties | **as you point to each coin to find out how many pence are in each row.**

 **p**

 **p**

 **p**

 **p**

 **p**

 **p**

NOW TRY THIS!

• **Write the answers in pounds.**

£   £   £   £   £   £

Teachers' note Practise counting on in twenties at the start of the lesson. Encourage the children to see that, when counting on from zero, the tens digits will always be even and the units/ones digit will be zero. Encourage them to use this as a strategy for checking. The children can use the number line at the top of the sheet to help them.

100% New Developing Mathematic
Counting and Understanding
Number: Ages 7–8
© A & C BLACK

Mixed up, missed out!

● **Two numbers in each sequence have been** | mixed up |.

1 Circle the two numbers.

| 0 | 10 | 20 | 30 | 40 | 50 | (70) | (60) | 80 | 90 | 100 | 110 |

| 0 | 50 | 100 | 150 | 200 | 250 | 300 | 350 | 450 | 400 | 500 | 550 |

| 0 | 20 | 40 | 60 | 80 | 100 | 120 | 160 | 140 | 180 | 200 | 220 |

| 0 | 30 | 60 | 90 | 120 | 150 | 180 | 210 | 240 | 300 | 270 | 330 |

| 0 | 40 | 80 | 120 | 160 | 240 | 200 | 280 | 320 | 360 | 400 | 440 |

● **Two numbers in each sequence have been** | missed out |.

2 Write the two numbers.

| 100 | 90 | 80 | _70_ | 60 | 50 | _40_ | 30 | 20 | 10 | 0 |

| 650 | 600 | 550 | 500 | 450 | 400 | 350 | 300 | ___ | ___ | 150 |

| 220 | 200 | 180 | 160 | ___ | 120 | 100 | 80 | ___ | 40 | 20 |

| 300 | 270 | 240 | 210 | ___ | 150 | 120 | ___ | 60 | 30 | 0 |

| 440 | 400 | ___ | ___ | 280 | 240 | 200 | 160 | 120 | 80 | 40 |

NOW TRY THIS!

● **Talk to a partner about patterns in these two sequences.**

| 0 | 20 | 40 | 60 | 80 | 100 | 120 | 140 | 160 | 180 | 200 | 220 |

| 0 | 40 | 80 | 120 | 160 | 200 | 240 | 280 | 320 | 360 | 400 | 440 |

Teachers' note This activity can follow on from work on counting in 2s, 3s, 4s and 5s. Encourage the children to notice patterns in the digits when they begin to count on in 20s, 30s, 40s and 50s.

**100% New Developing Mathematics
Counting and Understanding
Number: Ages 7–8
© A & C BLACK**

37

Multiple octopus

- **Start at 'zero' in the centre of the octopus.**
- Count on along each leg.

One leg has been done for you.

in 9s

in 2s

14 16 18 20

12

10

8

6

4

2

zero

9

8 7 6 5 4 3

in 3s

in 4s

in 8s

in 7s

in 6s

in 5s

NOW TRY THIS!

- **On which octopus leg or legs are these numbers?**

25 ___in 5s___   81 _____   6 __in 2s, 3s and 6s__

8 _____   9 _____   49 _____

35 _____   28 _____   36 _____

Teachers' note These octopus sheets make interesting displays. The children could use coloured paper to make their own large multiple octopuses for the classroom wall. Encourage them to look for particular numbers and to say on which leg or legs the number appears.

38

100% New Developing Mathematic Counting and Understanding Number: Ages 7–8
© A & C BLACK

Changing the guard

- **Fill in the missing numbers in each sequence.**

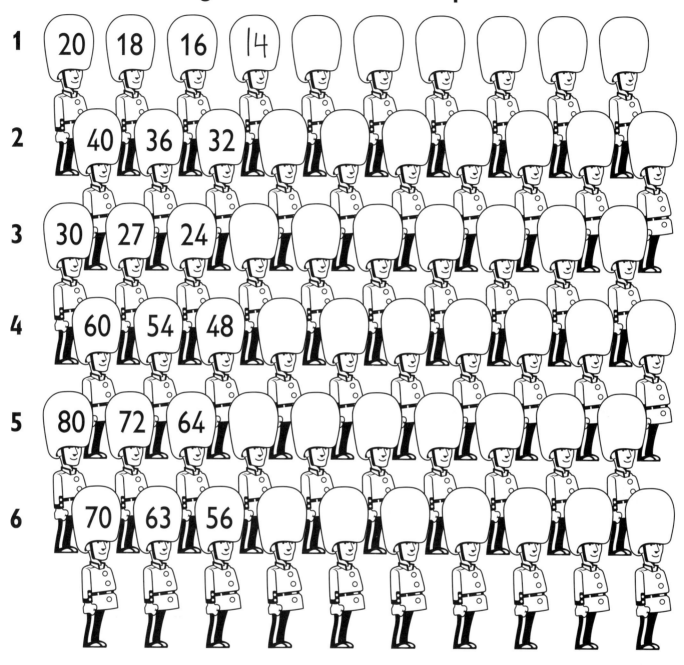

1 20 18 16 14

2 40 36 32

3 30 27 24

4 60 54 48

5 80 72 64

6 70 63 56

NOW TRY THIS!

- **Count back in** [nines] **from 90.**

90

Teachers' note This activity can be introduced practically (see page 9). As many children find counting backwards difficult, provide them with a 0–100 number line and encourage them to mark on the numbers to determine the pattern. For the extension activity, encourage the children to notice patterns in the digits of the numbers created.

100% New Developing Mathematics
Counting and Understanding
Number: Ages 7–8
© A & C BLACK

39

Superheroes

Hundreds Man is in charge of the **hundreds**

Tens Girl is in charge of the **tens**

Ones Boy is in charge of the **ones** (or units)

- **Partition these numbers to show the amount each superhero is in charge of.**

1

2 6 2

200 + 60 + 2

2

4 5 7

_____

3

9 3 1

_____

4

8 4 4

_____

5

6 0 5

_____

6

2 7 8

_____

7

1 3 7

_____

8

5 0 9

_____

9

8 8 8

_____

NOW TRY THIS!

- **Find two numbers from above with:**

3 tens _____ _____   2 hundreds _____ _____

7 ones _____ _____   no tens _____ _____

Teachers' note Children love the place value superheroes. Begin by choosing three children to represent the hundreds, tens and ones superheroes. Call out a number and ask the children to say how much each superhero is in charge of. Encourage children to notice that *Hundreds Man's* amount is always larger than *Tens Girl's* amount, whatever the digit (greater than 0).

100% New Developing Mathematics
Counting and Understanding
Number: Ages 7–8
© A & C BLACK

Partition pots: 1

You need
Partition pots: 2

- **Play this game with a partner.**
- **Cut out the cards and the gameboard.**

Gameboard for player 1

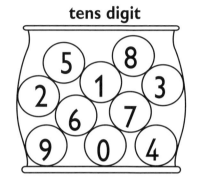

hundreds digit	tens digit	ones digit

114	**516**	**694**	**985**
807	**768**	**377**	**226**
523	**252**	**743**	**155**
931	**462**	**370**	**408**
99	**689**	**30**	**841**

Teachers' note Use this sheet in conjunction with page 42. The children work in pairs, each child choosing the player 1 or player 2 gameboard. The cards from both sheets are placed face down on the table. The children take turns to pick a card, choose one of its digits and colour that digit in the correct pot on their gameboard. The winner is the first player to colour all the digits in their pots.

100% New Developing Mathematics
Counting and Understanding
Number: Ages 7–8
© A & C BLACK

Partition pots: 2

You need
Partition pots: 1

- **Play this game with a partner.**
- **Cut out the cards and the gameboard.**

Gameboard for player 2

hundreds digit	tens digit	ones digit
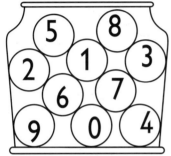		

562	609	919	980
131	828	732	841
53	493	87	775
519	624	394	165
400	357	246	276

Teachers' note This sheet should be used in conjunction with page 41.

100% New Developing Mathematics
Counting and Understanding
Number: Ages 7–8
© A & C BLACK

Digit snap!

• **Play this game with a partner.**

Your teacher will show you how to play the game.

You need
one pack of playing cards with the jokers, jacks, queens and kings taken out…

…and a copy of this worksheet each.

Hundreds	Tens	Ones

Teachers' note Show the children a pack of playing cards and explain that the ace stands for the digit 1. Demonstrate how to play the game (see page 9 for instructions) and encourage the children to say the three-digit numbers aloud as they play. As a whole-class activity, ask a range of questions about the children's recorded numbers (again, see page 9).

**100% New Developing Mathematics
Counting and Understanding
Number: Ages 7–8
© A & C BLACK**

Partition patterns

• **Continue each partition pattern.**

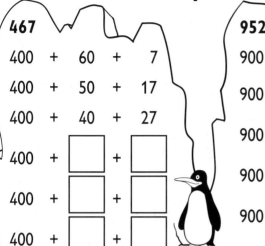

467
400 + 60 + 7
400 + 50 + 17
400 + 40 + 27
400 + ☐ + ☐
400 + ☐ + ☐
400 + ☐ + ☐

952
900 + 50 + 2
900 + ☐ + 12
900 + ☐ + 22
900 + ☐ + ☐
900 + ☐ + ☐
900 + ☐ + ☐

648
600 + 40 + 8
600 + ☐ + ☐
600 + ☐ + ☐
600 + ☐ + ☐

591
500 + 90 + 1
500 + ☐ + ☐
500 + ☐ + ☐
500 + ☐ + ☐
500 + ☐ + ☐
500 + ☐ + ☐
500 + ☐ + ☐
500 + ☐ + ☐

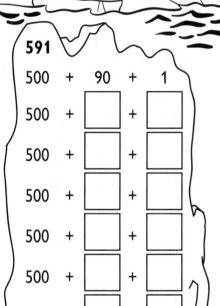

800
800 + 0 + 0
700 + 100 + 0
700 + 90 + 10
700 + 80 + ☐
700 + ☐ + ☐
700 + ☐ + ☐
700 + ☐ + ☐
700 + ☐ + ☐
700 + ☐ + ☐

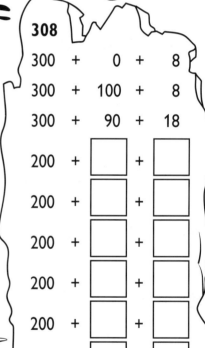

308
300 + 0 + 8
300 + 100 + 8
300 + 90 + 18
200 + ☐ + ☐
200 + ☐ + ☐
200 + ☐ + ☐
200 + ☐ + ☐
200 + ☐ + ☐
200 + ☐ + ☐

NOW TRY THIS!

• **Write a three-digit number on the back of this sheet. Make your own partition pattern.**

Teachers' note This skill is valuable for helping children to understand written methods of addition and subtraction. It is particularly useful as a way to begin subtracting, leading towards the decomposition method.

100% New Developing Mathematics Counting and Understanding Number: Ages 7–8
© A & C BLACK

Matchmakers

- **Cut out the cards.**
- **Sort them into groups with the same total.**

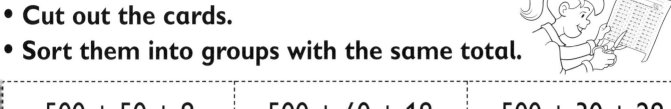

500 + 50 + 8	500 + 40 + 18	500 + 30 + 28
500 + 10 + 48	500 + 20 + 38	300 + 60 + 15
300 + 70 + 5	300 + 40 + 35	300 + 30 + 45
300 + 50 + 25	100 + 90 + 8	100 + 80 + 18
100 + 70 + 28	100 + 60 + 38	100 + 50 + 48
200 + 40 + 1	200 + 30 + 11	200 + 20 + 21
200 + 10 + 31	700 + 80 + 14	700 + 90 + 4
700 + 70 + 24	700 + 60 + 34	700 + 50 + 44
600 + 30 + 16	600 + 20 + 26	600 + 10 + 36
600 + 40 + 6	900 + 40 + 22	900 + 30 + 32
900 + 60 + 2	900 + 50 + 12	800 + 90 + 3
800 + 80 + 13	800 + 70 + 23	800 + 60 + 33
400 + 30 + 7	400 + 20 + 17	400 + 10 + 27

Teachers' note This activity encourages children to begin to realise how numbers can be partitioned into multiples of 100, 10 and 1 in different ways. If children are experiencing difficulty in sorting the cards into sets, ask them to take each card in turn and find the total. The cards can then be grouped according to totals and each set arranged to show partition patterns.

**100% New Developing Mathematics
Counting and Understanding
Number: Ages 7–8
© A & C BLACK**

45

Hedgehog numbers

• **Fill in the numbers hidden by the hedgehogs.**

$452 = 400 + 50 +$ 2

$394 = 300 + 90 +$

$354 = 300 + 50 +$

$354 = 300 + 40 +$

$507 = 400 + 100 +$

$452 = 400 + 40 +$

$275 = 200 +$ $+ 5$

$692 = 600 +$ $+ 2$

$596 = 500 +$ $+ 6$

$596 = 500 +$ $+ 16$

$467 = 400 +$ $+ 7$

$467 = 400 +$ $+ 17$

$751 = 600 + 150 +$

$874 = 700 + 170 +$

$863 = 700 + 160 +$

$784 = 600 + 170 +$

NOW TRY THIS!

• **Now try these.**

$881 = 700 +$ $+ 1$

$881 = 700 +$ $+ 11$

$738 =$ $+ 30 + 8$

$738 =$ $+ 130 + 8$

$697 =$ $+ 190 + 7$

$697 = 500 + 180 +$

Teachers' note This skill is valuable for helping children to understand written methods of addition and subtraction. It is particularly useful as a way to begin subtracting, leading towards the decomposition method. Ensure the children notice that the last four questions of the main activity involve more complex partitioning.

100% New Developing Mathematics
Counting and Understanding
Number: Ages 7–8
© A & C BLACK

Going crackers!

• **Write three-digit numbers on the crackers to make the statement** │true│ **.**

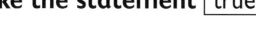

is 100 more than

is 100 more than

is 10 more than

is 10 more than

is 100 less than

is 100 less than

is 10 less than

is 10 less than

NOW TRY THIS!

• **Write numbers on the crackers to make these statements** │true│ **.**

is 200 more than

is 30 less than

is 6 more than

is 400 less than

is 300 less than

is 50 more than

is 90 less than

is 500 more than

Teachers' note This activity can be used as an open activity where children choose their own numbers to make the statements true. It encourages children to observe patterns, for example that when adding 100 to 321 only the hundreds digit changes. Alternatively, for some children specific numbers could be written onto one end of the cracker.

**100% New Developing Mathematics
Counting and Understanding
Number: Ages 7–8
© A & C BLACK**

Lifebelts

- **Round the number on the swimmer to the** nearest 10 .
- **Draw a line from the swimmer to the correct lifebelt.**

1

2

3

4

5

6

7

8

9

10

> **NOW TRY THIS!**
>
>

- **Write nine numbers that, when rounded to the** nearest 10 **, give the answer** 100 **.**

_____   _____   _____

Teachers' note Provide the children with a number line to help them with this activity. Ensure they understand that a number with a units digit of 5 rounds up to the nearest 10. At the end of the activity, call out two-digit numbers and ask the children to round them to the nearest 10.

100% New Developing Mathematics
Counting and Understanding
Number: Ages 7–8
© A & C BLACK

Rounders

• **Play this game with a partner.**

☆ Player 1 is 'squares' and player 2 is 'circles'.

☆ Take turns to roll the dice and move the counter around the pitch. Round the number to the **nearest 10**. If the answer is in a square, player 1 scores a point. If it is in a circle, player 2 scores a point.

You need one counter and a dice.

| 300 | (310) | 320 | (330) | 340 | (350) | 360 | (370) | 380 | (390) | 400 |

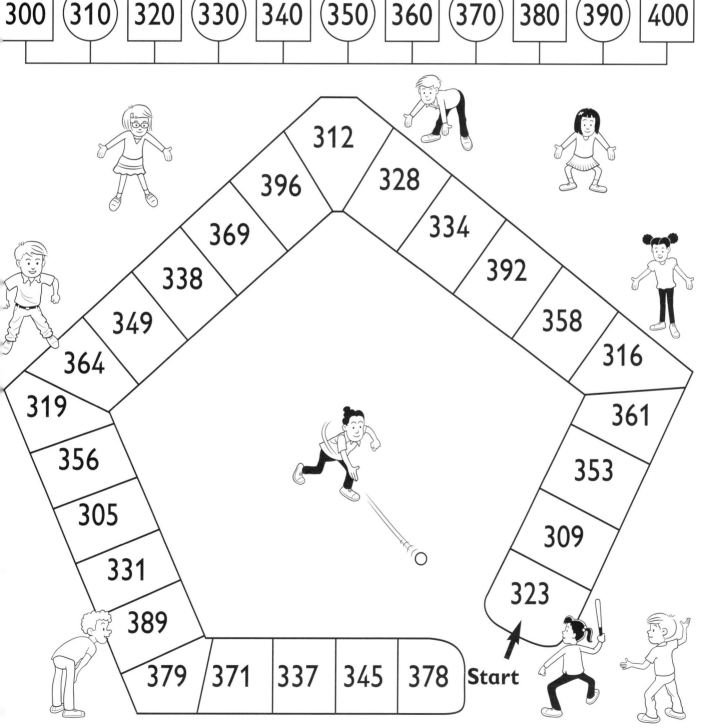

Numbers around the pitch: 312, 328, 396, 334, 369, 392, 338, 358, 349, 316, 364, 361, 319, 353, 356, 309, 305, 323, 331, 389, 379, 371, 337, 345, 378 **Start**

eachers' note Encourage the children to move around the board many times and to continue to
eep score. They can record their scores on scrap paper. The winner can be the first player to score
5 points.

100% New Developing Mathematics
Counting and Understanding
Number: Ages 7–8
© A & C BLACK

49

Rounding machine

- This machine rounds numbers to the   nearest 100 .
- For each input number, write the hundreds number it rounds to.

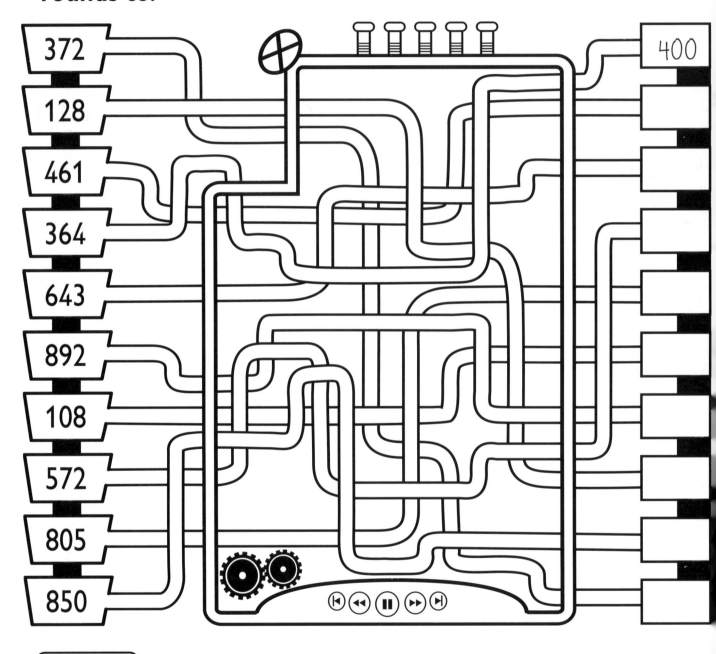

372 → 400

128

461

364

643

892

108

572

805

850

NOW TRY THIS!

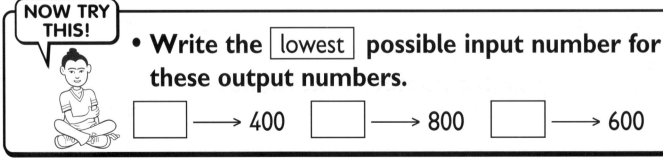

- Write the   lowest   possible input number for these output numbers.

☐ ——→ 400   ☐ ——→ 800   ☐ ——→ 600

Teachers' note Ensure the children understand that numbers ending in 50 round up to the nearest 100. At the end of the activity, call out three-digit numbers and ask the children to round them to the nearest 100 and to the nearest 10.

50

100% New Developing Mathematic Counting and Understanding Number: Ages 7–8
© A & C BLACK

Whose dog?

- **Round each number to the** | nearest 100 | **.**
- **Draw a line to join the dog to its owner.**

547

849

945

459

851

638

800

500

900

461

501

400

652

600

700

794

408

645

712

350

NOW TRY THIS!

- **On the dog, write the highest possible number that rounds to** | 400 | **.**

'eachers' note Ensure the children understand that numbers ending in 50 round up to the nearest 00. At the end of the activity, call out three-digit numbers and ask the children to round them to he nearest 100.

100% New Developing Mathematics Counting and Understanding Number: Ages 7–8
© A & C BLACK

51

Round and about

- **Round the numbers to the** nearest 10 **to help you estimate the answer.**

1

51 + 32 is about ☐

2

43 + 27 is about ☐

3

28 + 36 is about ☐

4

67 + 28 is about ☐

5

45 + 54 is about ☐

6

47 – 19 is about ☐

7

62 – 38 is about ☐

8

71 – 56 is about ☐

 NOW TRY THIS!

The answer to an addition question is about 150 **.**

- **Write four questions that could give this answer.**

_____   _____   _____   _____

Teachers' note Ensure the children notice that some questions on the page are additions and some are subtractions. At the start of the lesson, revise rounding numbers to the nearest 10 and show how this can help you make an estimate for a calculation.

100% New Developing Mathematic Counting and Understanding Number: Ages 7–8
© A & C BLACK

Rain rounding

- **Round the numbers to the** $\boxed{\text{nearest } 100}$ **to help you estimate the answers.**

1

134 + 291 is about ☐

2

361 + 117 is about ☐

3

451 + 268 is about ☐

4

312 + 658 is about ☐

5

275 + 539 is about ☐

6

674 − 352 is about ☐

7

631 − 492 is about ☐

8

855 − 545 is about ☐

9

953 − 448 is about ☐

10

928 − 674 is about ☐

NOW TRY THIS!

The answer to an addition question is $\boxed{\text{about } 1200}$ **.**

- **Write four questions that could give this answer.**

_____ _____ _____ _____

Teachers' note Ensure the children notice that some questions on the page are additions and some are subtractions. At the start of the lesson, revise rounding numbers to the nearest hundred and show how this can help you make an estimate for a calculation.

**100% New Developing Mathematics
Counting and Understanding
Number: Ages 7–8**
© A & C BLACK

Have a good trip!

These families go on a day trip. The distances show how far they travelled, before and after a stop.

• Round the numbers to the $\boxed{\text{nearest 100}}$ to help you estimate the total distance travelled.

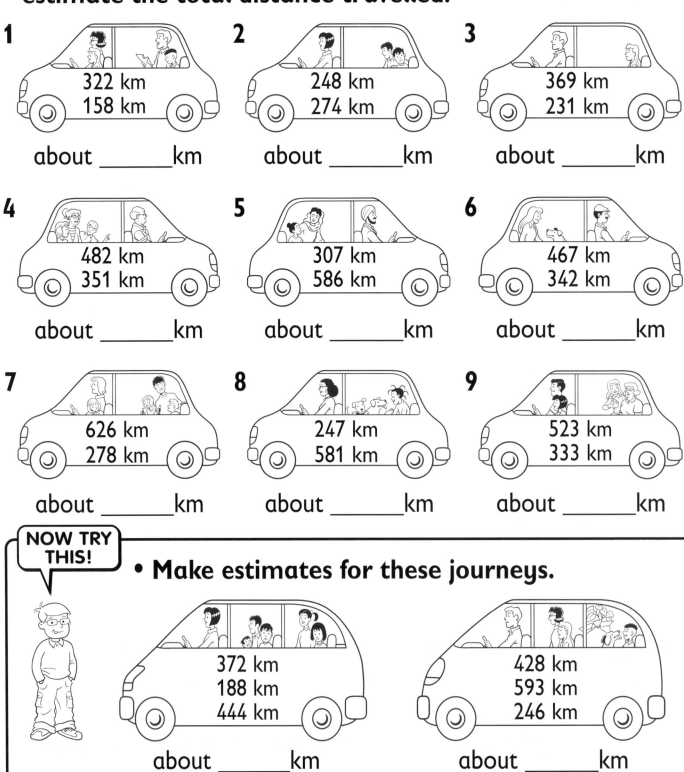

1
322 km
158 km

about _____ km

2
248 km
274 km

about _____ km

3
369 km
231 km

about _____ km

4
482 km
351 km

about _____ km

5
307 km
586 km

about _____ km

6
467 km
342 km

about _____ km

7
626 km
278 km

about _____ km

8
247 km
581 km

about _____ km

9
523 km
333 km

about _____ km

NOW TRY THIS!

• **Make estimates for these journeys.**

372 km
188 km
444 km

about _____ km

428 km
593 km
246 km

about _____ km

Teachers' note At the start of the lesson, revise rounding numbers to the nearest hundred and show how this can help you make an estimate for a calculation. Some children may find it easier to write the two rounded numbers first and then to add them. More confident children could round the numbers to the nearest 10.

100% New Developing Mathematic
Counting and Understanding
Number: Ages 7–8
© A & C BLACK

Eden has made some patterns
and shapes with triangular tiles.

- **Count the tiles and write what
  fraction of each shape is shaded.**

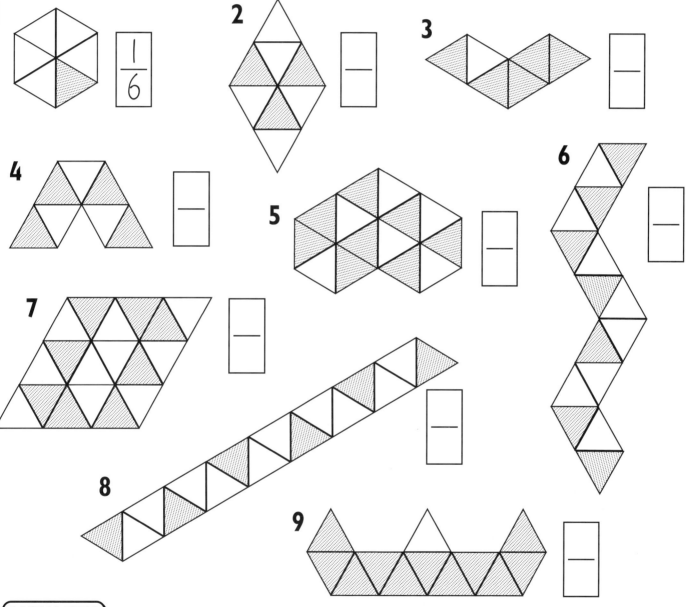

1 $\dfrac{1}{6}$

2 $\dfrac{}{}$

3 $\dfrac{}{}$

4 $\dfrac{}{}$

5 $\dfrac{}{}$

6 $\dfrac{}{}$

7 $\dfrac{}{}$

8 $\dfrac{}{}$

9 $\dfrac{}{}$

NOW TRY THIS!

- **Make some triangular tile puzzles of
  your own.**
- **Write what fraction of each shape is shaded.**

Teachers' note Watch out for the common error of writing the number of unshaded tiles as the denominator rather than the total number of tiles altogether, for example where 3 out of 7 tiles are shaded the children incorrectly write $\frac{3}{4}$ instead of $\frac{3}{7}$. The children will need isometric paper for the extension activity.

**100% New Developing Mathematics
Counting and Understanding
Number: Ages 7–8
© A & C BLACK**

Magic carpets

- **Cut out the cards.**
- **Match the fractions with the rug patterns to show what fraction is shaded.**

| $\dfrac{1}{6}$ | $\dfrac{5}{10}$ | $\dfrac{3}{4}$ | $\dfrac{13}{15}$ | $\dfrac{1}{9}$ | $\dfrac{10}{12}$ |
| $\dfrac{4}{7}$ | $\dfrac{2}{5}$ | $\dfrac{7}{12}$ | $\dfrac{5}{9}$ | $\dfrac{5}{12}$ | $\dfrac{3}{6}$ |

Teachers' note Watch out for the common error of writing the number of unshaded tiles as the denominator rather than the total number of tiles altogether, for example where 3 out of 7 tiles are shaded the children incorrectly write $\frac{3}{4}$ instead of $\frac{3}{7}$. See page 11 for an alternative game.

100% New Developing Mathematic Counting and Understanding Number: Ages 7–8
© A & C BLACK

Gee-up horse!

- ☐ Estimate ☐ **what fraction of the racecourse each horse has run.**

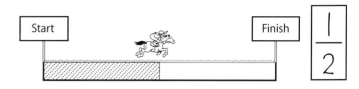 $\dfrac{1}{2}$

1

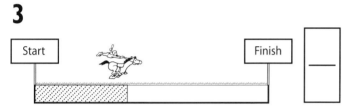 $\dfrac{\ }{\ }$

2

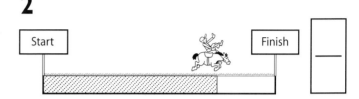 $\dfrac{\ }{\ }$

3

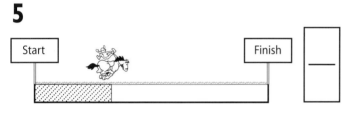 $\dfrac{\ }{\ }$

4

 $\dfrac{\ }{\ }$

5

 $\dfrac{\ }{\ }$

6

 $\dfrac{\ }{\ }$

7

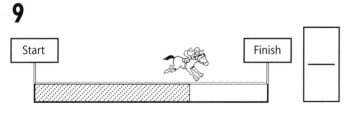 $\dfrac{\ }{\ }$

8

 $\dfrac{\ }{\ }$

9

 $\dfrac{\ }{\ }$

10

 $\dfrac{\ }{\ }$

NOW TRY THIS!

- **Shade this line so that about three-eighths is shaded.**

Teachers' note At the start of the lesson, hold up some strips of paper. Fold them into equal parts and ask the children to say what fraction of the whole strip each part is worth. Then hold up a strip that has a quarter shaded but has no fold marks. Encourage the children to estimate the fraction shaded and demonstrate by drawing lines to show where the fold marks would go.

**100% New Developing Mathematics
Counting and Understanding
Number: Ages 7–8
© A & C BLACK**

Fraction wall

- Write $>$ or $<$ between each pair of fractions to show which is more or less.

Example: $\dfrac{3}{4}$ $>$ $\dfrac{1}{2}$

1 whole							
$\frac{1}{2}$				$\frac{1}{2}$			
$\frac{1}{3}$		$\frac{1}{3}$			$\frac{1}{3}$		
$\frac{1}{4}$		$\frac{1}{4}$		$\frac{1}{4}$		$\frac{1}{4}$	
$\frac{1}{5}$		$\frac{1}{5}$	$\frac{1}{5}$		$\frac{1}{5}$		$\frac{1}{5}$
$\frac{1}{6}$	$\frac{1}{6}$		$\frac{1}{6}$	$\frac{1}{6}$		$\frac{1}{6}$	$\frac{1}{6}$
$\frac{1}{7}$	$\frac{1}{7}$	$\frac{1}{7}$	$\frac{1}{7}$	$\frac{1}{7}$	$\frac{1}{7}$	$\frac{1}{7}$	
$\frac{1}{8}$	$\frac{1}{8}$	$\frac{1}{8}$	$\frac{1}{8}$	$\frac{1}{8}$	$\frac{1}{8}$	$\frac{1}{8}$	$\frac{1}{8}$

1 $\dfrac{1}{2}$ ☐ $\dfrac{1}{4}$

2 $\dfrac{3}{8}$ ☐ $\dfrac{1}{4}$

3 $\dfrac{9}{10}$ ☐ $\dfrac{7}{8}$

4 $\dfrac{2}{5}$ ☐ $\dfrac{1}{3}$

5 $\dfrac{2}{3}$ ☐ $\dfrac{3}{4}$

6 $\dfrac{3}{10}$ ☐ $\dfrac{2}{5}$

7 $\dfrac{5}{6}$ ☐ $\dfrac{4}{5}$

8 $\dfrac{4}{8}$ ☐ $\dfrac{2}{5}$

9 $\dfrac{6}{10}$ ☐ $\dfrac{2}{3}$

10 $\dfrac{5}{8}$ ☐ $\dfrac{3}{4}$

11 $\dfrac{1}{6}$ ☐ $\dfrac{1}{5}$

12 $\dfrac{1}{8}$ ☐ $\dfrac{1}{10}$

13 $\dfrac{4}{6}$ ☐ $\dfrac{5}{8}$

14 $\dfrac{2}{3}$ ☐ $\dfrac{2}{5}$

15 $\dfrac{3}{5}$ ☐ $\dfrac{7}{10}$

16 $\dfrac{7}{8}$ ☐ $\dfrac{5}{6}$

17 $\dfrac{5}{8}$ ☐ $\dfrac{3}{5}$

18 $\dfrac{7}{10}$ ☐ $\dfrac{2}{3}$

NOW TRY THIS!

- Write four other fractions equivalent to $\dfrac{1}{2}$.

☐ ☐ ☐ ☐

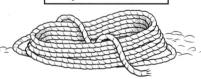

Teachers' note This page can be used in conjunction with coloured rods, such as Cuisenaire rods, so that the children can physically manipulate the fractional parts of a whole. If necessary, explain the term 'equivalent' as meaning 'worth the same'.

100% New Developing Mathematics Counting and Understanding Number: Ages 7–8 © A & C BLACK

Clever cylinders

These cylinders help you to find | equivalent | fractions.

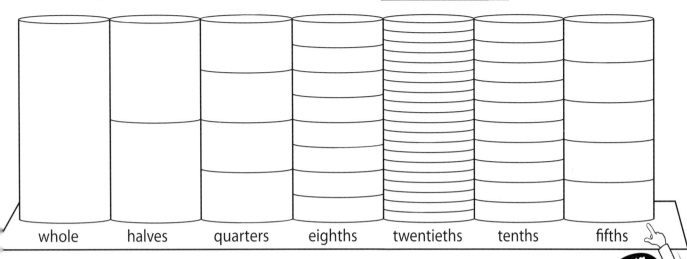

| whole | halves | quarters | eighths | twentieths | tenths | fifths |

1 Use the cylinders to help you fill in the missing numbers.

a 1 whole = [2] halves   **b** 3 quarters = [ ] eighths

c 1 quarter = [ ] eighths   **d** 2 eighths = [ ] twentieths

e 4 twentieths = [ ] tenths   **f** 4 tenths = [ ] fifths

g 3 fifths = [ ] tenths   **h** 4 fifths = [ ] tenths

i 9 tenths = [ ] twentieths   **j** 7 tenths = [ ] twentieths

2. Write four fractions equivalent to 1 half.

_____ = 1 half   _____ = 1 half

_____ = 1 half   _____ = 1 half

NOW TRY THIS!

- **On a separate piece of paper, rewrite all the equivalent statements above, like this:**

$$1a \quad 1 = \frac{2}{2}$$

Teachers' note Demonstrate how the diagram can be used to compare fractions, working from the bottom of each cylinder and looking across to find matching levels. If necessary, explain the term 'equivalent' as meaning 'worth the same'.

**100% New Developing Mathematics
Counting and Understanding
Number: Ages 7–8**
© A & C BLACK

Equivalent cards

- **Cut out the cards.**
- **Match** equivalent **pairs.**

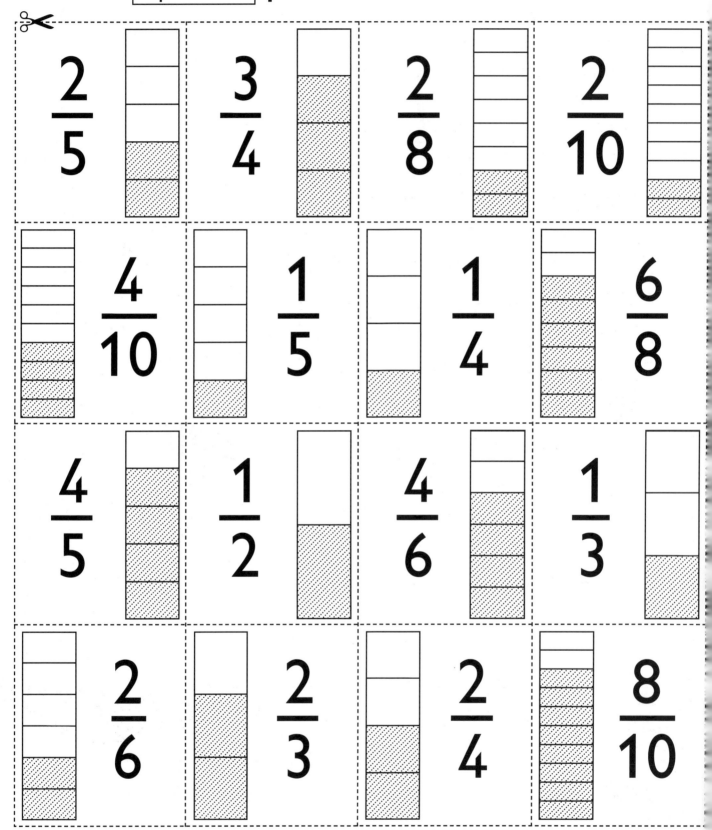

$$\frac{2}{5}$$

$$\frac{3}{4}$$

$$\frac{2}{8}$$

$$\frac{2}{10}$$

$$\frac{4}{10}$$

$$\frac{1}{5}$$

$$\frac{1}{4}$$

$$\frac{6}{8}$$

$$\frac{4}{5}$$

$$\frac{1}{2}$$

$$\frac{4}{6}$$

$$\frac{1}{3}$$

$$\frac{2}{6}$$

$$\frac{2}{3}$$

$$\frac{2}{4}$$

$$\frac{8}{10}$$

Teachers' note These cards can be used in a variety of ways, with children working individually or in pairs/groups (see page 11 for more information).

**100% New Developing Mathematics
Counting and Understanding
Number: Ages 7–8**
© A & C BLACK

Yo-ho-ho!

- ## **Play this game with a partner.**

☆ Each pick a treasure chest.

☆ Take turns to roll the dice and move
   your counter around the map.

☆ Work out the answer to the question, and if
   you can, cross off the answer in your treasure chest.

☆ The winner is the first player to cross off all their coins.

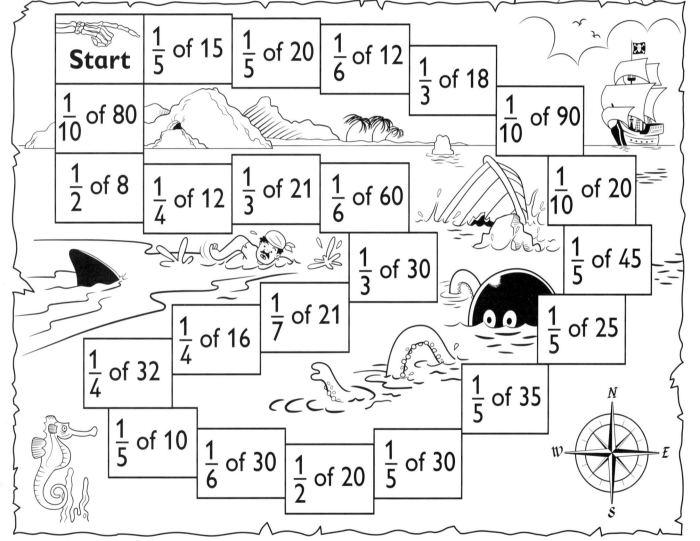

Start

$\frac{1}{5}$ of 15 $\frac{1}{5}$ of 20 $\frac{1}{6}$ of 12 $\frac{1}{3}$ of 18

$\frac{1}{10}$ of 80 $\frac{1}{10}$ of 90

$\frac{1}{2}$ of 8 $\frac{1}{4}$ of 12 $\frac{1}{3}$ of 21 $\frac{1}{6}$ of 60 $\frac{1}{10}$ of 20

$\frac{1}{3}$ of 30 $\frac{1}{5}$ of 45

$\frac{1}{7}$ of 21 $\frac{1}{5}$ of 25

$\frac{1}{4}$ of 16

$\frac{1}{4}$ of 32 $\frac{1}{5}$ of 35

$\frac{1}{5}$ of 10 $\frac{1}{6}$ of 30 $\frac{1}{2}$ of 20 $\frac{1}{5}$ of 30

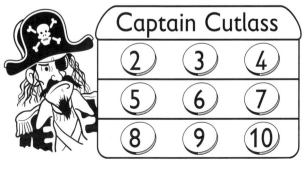

Captain Cutlass
(2) (3) (4)
(5) (6) (7)
(8) (9) (10)

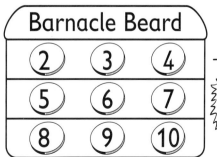

Barnacle Beard
(2) (3) (4)
(5) (6) (7)
(8) (9) (10)

Teachers' note Ensure the children understand that when finding a unit fraction of a number, they should divide the number into equal parts, according to the denominator, for example, $\frac{1}{5}$ of 20 is 20 divided by 5.

**100% New Developing Mathematics
Counting and Understanding
Number: Ages 7–8
© A & C BLACK**

Colourful kaleidoscopes

- **Colour the kaleidoscope to match the description.**

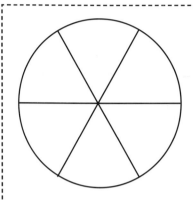

$\frac{1}{6}$ is red

$\frac{1}{2}$ is blue

$\frac{1}{3}$ is yellow

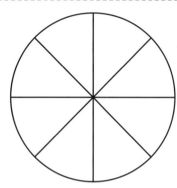

$\frac{1}{8}$ is red

$\frac{3}{8}$ is blue

$\frac{1}{2}$ is yellow

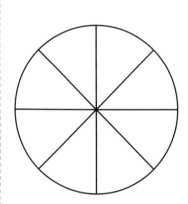

$\frac{2}{8}$ is red

$\frac{1}{2}$ is blue

$\frac{1}{4}$ is yellow

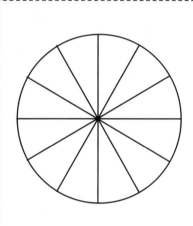

$\frac{1}{12}$ is red

$\frac{1}{2}$ is blue

$\frac{1}{6}$ is yellow

$\frac{1}{4}$ is orange

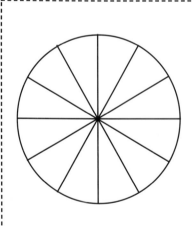

$\frac{5}{12}$ is red

$\frac{1}{6}$ is blue

$\frac{1}{4}$ is yellow

$\frac{2}{12}$ is orange

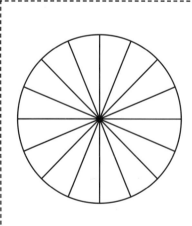

$\frac{2}{16}$ is red

$\frac{1}{8}$ is blue

$\frac{1}{4}$ is yellow

$\frac{1}{2}$ is orange

NOW TRY THIS!

- **Make some more kaleidoscope patterns and describe them using fractions.**

Teachers' note This activity can really test a child's understanding of fractions. There are a variety of ways in which children can work out how many sections to shade in each colour. One way is to ask the children to find fractions of number, for example by finding $\frac{1}{4}$ of 8 or $\frac{1}{6}$ of 12. For more information, see page 11.

**100% New Developing Mathematics
Counting and Understanding
Number: Ages 7–8
© A & C BLACK**

Answers

p 15
Now try this!

'One fine day a fat rat sat on a gnat'

p 17

8		7	0	6		1	5	8
5	2	9		4	1	0		9
0		9	4	1		0		9
			7		6	0	9	
	6	9	9		4		9	6
5		0		2	0	0		7
9	4	1		7			5	0
9				5	7	9		5

p 19
38	193	611	722
249	879	635	529

p 20
HEART
SPORT
EIGHT
STEAM
PEARS

p 21
172, 179, 182, 184, 197, 200
100, 417, 427, 472, 714, 741
324, 342, 343, 442, 443, 444
506, 565, 566, 605, 656, 665
777, 780, 787, 807, 870, 878
Now try this!
656, 665, 714, 741, 777, 780, 787, 807

p 22

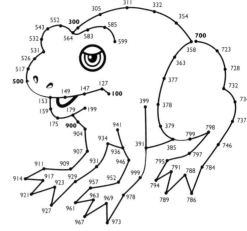

p 25
325, 352, 456, 635, 652
808, 910, 981, 1001, 1010
1011, 1020, 1050, 1120, 1210
Now try this!
1542, 1190, 1001, 987, 897,
1600, 1060, 1016, 1006, 610
8342, 8243, 4283, 2843, 2483

p 28
1	orange	yellow	red
	blue	yellow	red
2	orange	yellow	green
	red	orange	yellow

Now try this!
green	blue	red
green	green	blue

p 30
1 5, 10, 15, 20, 25, 30, 35, 40
2 55, 60, 65, 70, 75, 80, 85, 90
3 115, 120, 125, 130, 135, 140, 145, 150
Now try this!
Lola	Li
Raz	Alice
Josh	Alice

p 33
28	70	44	26

Now try this!
1, 7, 13, 19, 25, 31, 37

p 34
0, 7, 14, 21, 28, 35, 42,
49, 56, 63, 70, 77, 84, 91
98, 105, 112, 119, 126, 133, 140
161, 154, 147, 140, 133, 126, 119,
112, 105, 98, 91, 84, 77, 70,
Now try this!
14, 63, 140, 147, 175

p 35
49   64   63   72   56   72   80
Now try this!
21, 28, 35, 42, 49, 56
24, 32, 40, 48, 56, 64
27, 36, 45, 54, 63, 72

p 36
| 120p | 200p | 160p |
| 220p | 240p | 300p |

Now try this!
| £1.20 | £2.00 | £1.60 | £2.20 |
| £2.40 | £3.00 | | |

p 37
1 60, 70   400, 450   140, 160
      270, 300   200, 240
2 70, 40   250, 200   140, 60
      180, 90   360, 320
Now try this!
When counting on from zero in 40s the numbers are double the numbers in the 20s.

The numbers are all multiples of 10 and all have even digits (apart from zero).

p 38
Now try this!
in 5s   in 9s   in 2s, 3s and 6s
in 2s, 4s and 8s   in 3s and 9s   in 7s
in 5s and 7s   in 4s and 7s   in 4s, 6s and 9s

p 39
1 14, 12, 10, 8, 6, 4, 2,
2 28, 24, 20, 16, 12, 8, 4
3 21, 18, 15, 12, 9, 6, 3

4 42, 36, 30, 24, 18, 12, 6
5 56, 48, 40, 32, 24, 16, 8
6 49, 42, 35, 28, 21, 14, 7
Now try this!
90, 81, 72, 63, 54, 45, 36, 27, 18, 9

p 40
1 200 + 60 + 2	**2** 400 + 50 + 7	**3** 900 + 30 + 1
4 800 + 40 + 4	**5** 600 + 0 + 5	**6** 200 + 70 + 8
7 100 + 30 + 7	**8** 500 + 0 + 9	**9** 800 + 80 + 8

Now try this!
931 and 137   262 and 278
457 and 137   605 and 509

p 46
2	4	4	14	7	12
70	90	90	80	60	50
1	4	3	14		

Now try this!
| 180 | 170 | 700 |
| 600 | 500 | 17 |

p 54
| **1** 500 | **2** 500 | **3** 600 | **4** 900 | **5** 900 |
| **6** 800 | **7** 900 | **8** 800 | **9** 800 | |

Now try this!
1000   1200

p 55
1 1/6   **2** 3/8   **3** 5/6   **4** 4/7   **5** 8/14   **6** 7/15
7 8/18   **8** 6/16   **9** 11/12

p 57
1 1/4   **2** 3/4   **3** 2/5   **4** 1/5   **5** 1/3   **6** 1/6
7 1/10   **8** 9/10   **9** 2/3   **10** 1/8

p 58
1 >	**2** >	**3** >	**4** >	**5** <	**6** <
7 >	**8** >	**9** <	**10** <	**11** <	**12** >
13 >	**14** >	**15** <	**16** >	**17** >	**18** >

p 59
1 a 2   b 6   c 2   d 5   e 2   f 2
     g 6   h 8   i 18   j 14